GETTING WHAT YOU WANT IN LIFE . . .
WITHOUT FEELING GUILTY

A workbook for breaking out of codependency and other negative patterns

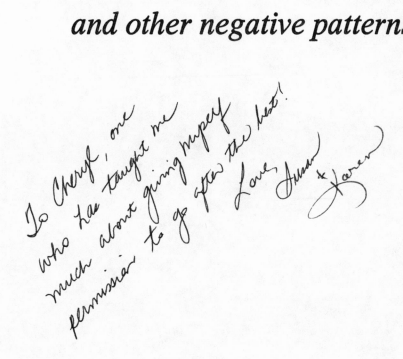

To Cheryl, one who has taught me much about giving myself permission to go after the best! Love, Susan & Karen

By

KAREN W. POOL

SUSAN C. ELIASON

Illustrated and designed by

JERRY T. CHRISTOPHERSON

To the men in our lives
who motivated us to write this book

About the Authors

Karen W. Pool loves books and even reads while waiting in line at the post office or the bank! She is always learning and asking questions. She enjoys talking about ideas and spending time with family and friends. She grew up on a farm in Wyoming and likes a bit of earth to grow her own fruits and vegetables. As she grows older, she believes her happiness comes from a combination of: a firm belief in Christ and gospel living, family relationships, and personal growth experiences. Making choices and taking responsibility has been her best growth experience of the past few years and she never thought life could be so fun and challenging all at the same time. Karen has a Masters Degree in Home Economics and Instructional Science from Brigham Young University and is currently working as the Gender Equity Coordinator at Utah Valley Community College, Orem, Utah. She provides inservice training for fifteen school districts for the state with two assignments: (1) to assist teachers in eliminating bias and stereotyping from their classrooms, and (2) to teach the process of self-reliance to young women ages fourteen to twenty-five. She does public speaking and freelance curriculum writing, yet with all that she is learning to rest and take care of herself better. She is married to Stan Pool and they have four children.

Susan C. Eliason is gentleness, intensity, and sparkling blue eyes combined. She is the refining editor of the group with an eye for detail, and a passion for words—speaking them, writing them, even creating and combining them into new funny forms—like "nagivator" for instance (her name for a backseat driver!). Susan celebrates the end of a writing project by gathering the stubs of the pencils she used in the process and preserving them as ready evidence of her effort. She has a passion for legal thrillers, jet fighters and hot bubble baths and goes out of her way to step on crunchy leaves in the fall. She knows when she is in love because she can't help writing poetry. Susan holds a Masters Degree in Organizational Behavior and is currently employed at Brigham Young University as a developer of instruction. She has designed and presented numerous training management programs in the United States, Japan, and South Korea, and enjoys freelance writing and public speaking.

At age thirty, **Jerry T. Christopherson** went back to school—taking one class at a time—fitting them in between family responsibilities. (She is married to Vernon Christopherson and has six children and recently got a granddaughter!) She graduated with honors when she was forty, receiving a Bachelor of Fine Arts degree from Brigham Young University. At home she had always been creative with her art—figuring out fancy ways to make bread, toys, and costumes for her children. Even before she received her degree, she was competitive in her field of design and illustration. She began her professional illustrating career in 1980 when her first children's book was published. She has designed and illustrated thirteen books since then and worked as a staff artist for the Missionary Training Center of the LDS Church. Jerry is working on her Masters degree at Syracuse University and will graduate in August of 1992. Presently she is teaching design and illustration in the Clothing and Textiles Department at BYU. Jerry loves being involved, growing and stretching, being creative, and organizing and planning activities. Her friends characterize her as persistent, enthusiastic, and a delightful person to brainstorm with. Whenever Karen and Susan were stumped in writing, they would brainstorm with Jerry.

As the three of them became friends several years ago, they would walk together and talk about their dreams and the growing, enriching experiences they were having since they learned that they could get what they wanted in life and didn't need to feel guilty about wanting what they wanted. The ideas for a workbook to share those principles began when they were climbing hills together. Being women of action they were soon moving ahead and this workbook is the result!

TABLE OF CONTENTS

INTRODUCTION

Suppose you were about to begin the most exciting journey of your life—the trip you had anticipated for years. You had seen others embark on similar adventures; you had read the stories and heard the songs about the glamour and thrill of it all. And now, finally, it's *your* turn. You run for the platform, eagerly climb aboard, turn around and wave farewell to those left behind. The exodus has begun. But when things don't work out exactly right, you realize that those travel plans you made long ago with such haste and anticipation lacked two essential components—

a MAP and a DESTINATION.

This workbook will help you determine your destination and draw your own map. Creating this workbook has been a joyful learning process. Because of our own experiences, we encourage the idea that women can design the patterns of their lives. We call this process "life planning" or "mapping." Like the journey that begins without a map or destination, the result of uncharted life planning can be an adventure or a disaster, depending mostly on unpredictable events and situations that will arise. By defaulting to "reactive" planning, our trips—and our lives—can have the most unlikely outcomes.

We plan to marry and have a family, for example. Then when the spouse does not appear, or disappears, or the children come and go, we may find ourselves stuck in a holding pattern or otherwise unprepared for the rest of the journey of life. We may then develop unproductive behavior patterns in an unconscious attempt to protect ourselves or to just survive. Maintaining these patterns can be unproductive and unhealthy. One such behavior pattern, codependency, results from a compulsive need to control things and people outside ourselves to the point of self-neglect.

Although codependency was originally associated with the behavior of a spouse in an alcoholic family, it has expanded to include dependence on any compulsive behavior found in dysfunctional families that results in sacrificing our best self-interests. As women, we learn to control others by becoming caretakers. Needing to control and fix those around us and not taking care of ourselves can have far-reaching negative effects. When we "need" others—their approval, their dutiful obedience to our way of thinking, their adherence to our standards—to feel secure and happy, we are being codependent.

Initially, the idea of taking care of ourselves (rather than everyone but ourselves) can be difficult to accept. For women who have been taught by society to gain approval by taking care of others, the concept of individual responsibility can be foreign and even threatening. We may see doing things for ourselves, wanting things for ourselves, thinking for ourselves, as selfish and feel guilty when we take even the smallest steps toward self- care. But we can let go of feeling guilty. True caring for others begins with caring for *self*.

When we're ready to grow, to take care of ourselves, and to eliminate codependency, we may seek the guidance of others for deeper understanding. This can be helpful if we also acknowledge that the truest answers for each of us come from within. And when we tune into these inner voices, we also become attuned to spiritual answers. When we're not used to tuning into ourselves for answers, though, it can be scary and difficult to begin the process.

We suggest that you take time to write out your thoughts and feelings, wants and desires—and then accept responsibility for your own happiness. This means letting go of the impossible goal of fixing or controlling everyone else and taking an honest look at the life you have lived to this point. Look at what you have loved, what you would change, and discover what you want to have happen in your life.

So this workbook is meant for you, to help you explore the possibilities and choices awaiting you now and in the future. It includes plenty of questions only you can answer and room for you to record your thoughts and feelings as you go along. Each chapter in this workbook is a different beginning place to help you become more self-aware and more caring about yourself. The chapters are divided into subsections that include exercises of one page or less. Authors of many self-help books suggest writing answers to questions and activities in another notebook or journal as you read their work. We have included the writing space *within* the pages of this book and a list of additional reading resources at the end of each chapter.

Finding the answers takes practice and effort. The results, though, are increased self-confidence, love and acceptance for yourself and those around you, peace of mind, and happiness. Design your life journey—and enjoy the trip!

GETTING
WHAT YOU
WANT IN LIFE
(WITHOUT WAITING TO BE TOLD)

Profiles

These women have been surprised at life's circumstances and are not sure what to do next:

Doris has all five children in school now—two of them in college. Seeing her family growing older and needing her less has left Doris questioning her value and purpose and wondering where to focus her energy.

Paula always felt that she would be a stay-at-home mother with lots of kids. She just turned thirty though and hasn't married yet.

Alese has three small children under six, including a fussy five-month-old baby. She is tired all the time. Her husband is away from home a lot, and Alese feels resentful that she has to manage everything alone so much.

Ranae was an A student. She planned to win a scholarship and eventually attend law school. But she didn't anticipate the consequences of becoming pregnant during her senior year of high school.

Whether single, married, widowed, or disabled; whether we have children or not, we all will face times in our lives when we won't know exactly what we want. At those times we wish that someone could just tell us which direction to go on our personal "yellow-brick road"—someone more reliable than the straw man.

The fact is, most of us spend our lives doing what we are told to do while waiting for permission—from parents, husbands, well-meaning friends and relatives, and society— to do things God has already given us permission to do. This chapter is a beginning place for some personal exploration in the following areas: giving yourself permission, accepting responsibility, changing the rules, figuring out what you want, eliminating shoulds, practicing brainstorming, and modeling behavior.

Being out of touch with what you want is a major symptom of codependency. You may not know what your desires really are. You may have postponed figuring them out. Paradoxically, though, fear of the future fades once you figure out what you want, then prepare a plan to succeed. Preparation is a protection against future crises. Answers will come from within as you give yourself permission to explore thoughts and feelings. You can choose to do many good things that you really want to do.

Giving yourself permission

You may not be asked very often what you want in life. Of course, there are many willing to advise you about what you *should* want. They compare you to themselves and express genuine concern. They want to be a support. Still, no one knows you as well as you can know yourself.

There is a way to look inside and discover your own desires, dreams, and values. It's as simple as giving yourself permission to take charge of your life. If you've never taken this kind of initiative before, your first reaction could be a mixture of excitement *and* fear. The fear may surface in thoughts such as "I can't," "It's too scary," "I would be a total failure," "It's too much responsibility." Your feelings are real, so take a deep breath and read on.

You may be like many women who don't get a lot of practice figuring out what they want or think or feel. You're too busy taking care of everyone else, solving others' problems, controlling and manipulating others' lives, pleasing everyone else, or putting what you want on hold because it would be selfish to take care of *you*. Actually, it's healthy to explore your own viewpoint about life and what's ahead—to think about . . .

> what *you* want to do,
> who *you* want to be with,
> who *you* want to be.

You can do it at your own pace, in your own time—"baby step" by "baby step," if necessary. All it takes is practice.

Use the following categories as a beginning place to brainstorm about education, career, marriage, home, family, and life in general. Give yourself permission to honestly evaluate your feelings. This process is the launching pad for your journey. It is the first step in taking charge of your life.

Things in my life I'm certain about

Things in my life I'm uncertain about

Questions I want answers to

People I can talk to for more information

Accepting responsibility

Not knowing what you want is like wearing blinders. As long as you refuse to look at what you want, it's easy to avoid responsibility when things don't work out exactly right. Avoiding responsibility keeps you stuck and unhappy. When you make a conscious choice to become involved in your own life, to make your own decisions, you become responsible.

You can choose to be responsible for your own happiness, for instance, instead of blaming everyone around you or your circumstances for your unhappiness. It begins with being in charge of yourself—answering for your acts and decisions. Can you remember a time recently when you took responsibility for—

—keeping your promise to someone?
—avoiding something that was bad for your health?
—admitting you made a mistake?
—stopping behavior that was hurting someone else?
—changing a personal habit for the better?

Take a minute to jot down your impressions, your dreams, and your desires in the following areas. Imagine where you want to be in each category (including those you add) now and on down the road:

WHAT I WANT	NOW	IN 5 YEARS
Family		
School/Job		
Financially		
Relationships		

Changing the rules

As the caretakers in our society, women may accept ideas that instruct them against self-care and clarity of purpose. In families, our behaviors and sometimes our lives are directed by an unwritten set of rules. Rarely are these rules positive. In fact, the most common of these unwritten rules have been referred to by therapists as "the rules of codependency." In her book, *Beyond Codependency*, Melody Beattie identifies several of these rules:

—Avoid feeling or talking about feelings,
—Don't think, figure things out, or make decisions for yourself,
—Don't be who you are because that's not good enough,
—Don't be selfish, put yourself first, say what you want and need, or take care of yourself,
—Don't be honest and direct—hint, manipulate, and make assumptions about what other
  people want and expect from you,
—Don't disrupt the system by growing or changing (pp. 93-94).

When you seek to define yourself clearly and take care of yourself, you give yourself permission to change unhealthy rules. You then develop a sense of well-being and confidence in small but significant areas that allows you to deal with the major issues, including relationships, careers, and childbearing. Part of discovering what you want means exploring your own ideas, desires, and opinions. Answer the following open-ended questions with the first thing that comes to mind:

1. When I receive a compliment, I

2. Secretly I wish

3. What I like most about my body is

4. If I wanted a hug from someone, I would

5. What scares me most about what I'll be doing five years from now is

6. If I were to do something different from my parents' relationship in my own marriage, I would

7. Other people hurt me most when they

8. The traits I admire most in other people include

9. To get other people's approval, I

10. The part I want religion to play in my life would include

11. The goals money can help me realize include

12. I daydream most about

Figuring out what you want

There are ways to break out of limiting codependent patterns and figure out what you want.

"You have the power to create a life of your choice—to get what you really want, not just what you're handed.... It is dependent only upon the full use of your creative imagination. Thought is energy. . . . Only thought stands in your way of attaining what you want on mental, physical, emotional, spiritual, and financial levels. You can have what you think you deserve and what you believe you can have. Conversely, if you are convinced you shouldn't have, or are unworthy of getting, what you want, you will unconsciously arrange to put whatever you need in your path to prevent your becoming successful" (Ross, pp. *1,6,9*).

Taking time to think and imagine may be difficult at first. You may be well practiced at "doing things"—homemaking, PTA meetings, entertaining family and business associates, mending, gathering resources for a community project, or caring for the sick. There is no end to what must be done and you may feel obligated to do it all! While there is much that is of value in contributing to the lives of others, it's healthy to think about and imagine and include things you *like* to do that contribute to the quality of your life.

A friend was asked to complete the worksheet on the next page by writing the things she liked to do. She found that there was much in her routine of caring for family and neighbors that she did without thinking whether or not she "liked" it. She loved certain outcomes—a clean house, for example—but when asked if she loved to *clean* house, she said no and that whether she liked it or not didn't matter. It was more important to *have* a clean house than to *like cleaning* house. While that point of view has validity, it made it difficult for her to identify things that she really liked to do; doing what she liked hadn't been on her mind for years!

If it has been a long time since you have included things you like to do in your life, you may first experience anger at the decisions that have been made on behalf of others at the expense of your own desires, talents, and abilities. Feelings of anger and resentment are clues that something in your life needs to change. It's OK to make these changes appropriately. We can do it without harming others, although as we begin to allow time for ourselves, we may be criticized at first.

Things you like to do [*]

It is helpful to assess whether or not you are doing anything in your life right now that is a pleasure for you (even if it is part of your work or family responsibilities). Including things you like to do among all the responsibilities and "required" things adds to your contentment and joy. These are things that make you glad to be alive, and they may be different for each individual. Write fifteen things you like to do (in any order). Next, write a statement describing whether you do this alone or with someone, for work or pleasure, and if you are doing it now or would like to be doing it.

Example: backpacking	*I like to do this with friends for recreation, not doing it now.*
Example: trying new recipes	*I would like to publish a best-selling cookbook*
1.	
2.	
3.	
4.	
5.	
6.	
7.	
8.	
9.	
10.	
11.	
12.	
13.	
14.	
15.	

*Adapted from *Wishcraft* by Barbara Sher, p. 46

If you are already doing a number of things you really enjoy, give yourself a pat on the back. If your life doesn't include much to stretch you (or relax you) and leave you with a sense of personal satisfaction, then look over the list you have written and pick a place to start. When you begin, you may find yourself initially using all kinds of negative messages, such as "I can't, there's not enough money or time" when what you may really be saying is: "I don't deserve this," or "It's too frightening." Be honest about your feelings and allow yourself time to work through your negative thinking. Then set a date in the near future when you will begin the first step toward doing something you like, including some more specific daydreaming. Perhaps it will be finding a partner to play racquetball with once a week, starting a book club, researching your great-grandmother's life story, taking a class, or just taking a nap.

Eliminating shoulds

When we face major decisions, we often ask "should" questions: Should I get married? Should I go to college? Should I look for a job? *and* daily we make "should" statements: I should be getting better grades, I should do something nice for my mother, I should be more patient with my husband, or I should take better care of my health. "Should" questions and statements recognize a dilemma but create no solution. They imply that we have no choice in the matter. When we say to ourselves (or to someone else), "I really should get more organized," what we are really saying is, "I should . . . , but I'm not going to!" (Helmstetter, p. 75).

As caretakers, we are continually bombarded by society, the media, and our families with our deficiencies—our dirty collars, our deprived children, our outdated clothing and furniture—to the point that we absorb mountains of unhealthy guilt for all we are not getting done or fixing. This kind of guilt can be overwhelming and a drain on our energy. When we begin to eliminate the "shoulds" from our lives and replace them with what we want to do, and can do, we free trapped energy that can be used in more productive ways.

It's important to learn how to change *"I should"* to *"I want"* or *"What do I want to have happen?"* or *"I could"* and *"I feel"* statements. This helps to change the focus by looking at the result as well as the activity or decision.

Change the statements on the following page from *"I should"* to "I want . . . ," or "I could . . . ," and "This is how I feel. . . ."

Include some of your own "shoulds" you want to change, such as "I should lose weight."

-
-
-
-

Changing shoulds to coulds and wants

1. *I should get to work on time.*
   - I want

   - I feel

2. *I should lose weight.*
   - I could

   - What I want to have happen is

3. *I should study harder.*
   - I want

   - I feel

4. *I should be a better housekeeper.*
   - I could

   - What I want to have happen is

5. *I ought to write or call home more often.*
   - I want

   - I feel

6. *I should get married.*
   - I could

   - What I want to have happen is

7. *I know I ought to find a different job.*
   - I want

   - I feel

8. *I should . . .*
   - I could

   - What I want to have happen is

9. *I should . . .*
   - I want

   - I feel

10. *I should . . .*
    - I could

    - What I want to have happen is

11. *I should . . .*
    - I want

    - I feel

12. *I should . . .*
    - I could

    - What I want to have happen is

Practicing brainstorming

When you give yourself permission to take charge of your life, you are suddenly faced with a myriad of increased options. Brainstorming is a way of uncovering options—of recognizing your possibilities. Brainstorming is creative thinking. It is a technique used to generate all kinds of ideas. These ideas, in turn, can open us up to other possibilities. Brainstorming with yourself or with others helps you think of ways and means you may not have considered to solve problems or accomplish tasks. Begin by writing in the space below three problems or decisions you face right now. These may involve relationships, schooling, a job, or anything else important to you.

————————————————

————————————————

————————————————

You may have written (or thought of) your problem like this: "I can't go to college because I don't have a job, I don't have money, I don't have a scholarship. . . ." In her book *Wishcraft*, Barbara Sher suggests that an "I can't" statement is a dead end. Your brain doesn't work with it. So learn instead to work with "I can" statements (p. 76).

1. How can I _____?
2. How can I _____?

Here's an example:

1. How can I get my degree without $20,000?
2. How can I get $20,000?

* * *

This may take some practice but begin with one problem and write down every idea that comes into your head, no matter how silly or farfetched. This is basic brainstorming, the simplest form of a proven technique for using your head to solve problems.

* * *

Modeling behavior

The best way to motivate those around you to grow and achieve and create (and give themselves permission to figure out what *they* want) is to be growing and achieving *yourself*. When you say, "I can't," "It's too hard," "I don't have time," or "It's too late for me," your children will do the same. Whatever you say you can do, though, they will try also.

"If you are always doing something for others and never anything for yourself, you can make them physically comfortable, but cannot affect them spiritually. For to teach, encourage, cheer up, console, amuse, stimulate or advise a husband or children or friends, you have to be something yourself. And how to be something yourself? Only by working hard and with gumption at something you love and care for and think is important.

"So if you want your children to be musicians, then work at music yourself, seriously and with all your intelligence. If you want them to be scholars, study hard yourself. If you want them to be honest, be honest yourself. And so it goes.

"If you would shut your door against the children for an hour a day and say: 'Mother is working on her five-act tragedy in blank verse!' you would be surprised how they would respect you. They would probably all become playwrights." (Ueland, pp. 99-100)

Getting what you want begins with thinking, asking questions, and writing things down. "Writing down" is important; you gain insights from writing you can't get from contemplation. This process can help you identify codependency patterns that may be holding you back from reaching your full potential. Realize also that as you grow and change, the things you want in life will change also.

Thoreau stated, "Most people live lives of quiet desperation—they die with their music still in them." You begin letting your music out by giving yourself permission to grow, by practicing, and by being an example of healthy, appropriate self-caring. Write a summary of what you have learned about yourself in the previous exercises in the column to the right.

Additional Reading:

Prospering Woman
by Ruth Ross

Wishcraft
by Barbara Sher

*What To Say
When You Talk To Yourself*
by Shad Helmstetter

Beyond Codependency
by Melody Beattie

RECOGNIZING THE WOMAN IN THE MIRROR
(IDENTIFYING PERSONAL VALUES)

Profiles

June watched anxiously as her husband lectured their teenage son in the kitchen. She and George have such different views on disciplining their children.

Janelle was fifty-nine and widowed after forty years of marriage. She felt lost without her husband even though he had been bedridden with cancer the past eighteen months. Friends and relatives all had suggestions about where she should turn her focus now.

Kim wanted to move away from home. Her boyfriend wanted her to move into his apartment. She felt uneasy and knew her parents would not approve, yet she couldn't decide what to do; she didn't want to hurt his feelings or lose him.

Part of knowing ourselves is discovering what we consider important. It is helpful to assess our values—our beliefs and feelings of what is important—throughout our lives. Values guide our actions and attitudes and are reflected in our interactions with others. Our values can provide a standard to direct our lives if we know what they are.

To clarify what we mean, let's compare values to the principles of design. By knowing the basic principles of design and what looks good on us, for instance, we are not swayed by the media's subtle pressure each year to wear this season's latest colors and fashions. In the same way, when we identify what is important, we are not tossed about by everyone else's opinions. When we decide what's important for us individually, we are not desperate for outward approval; we gain confidence from an inner source of approval.

When we are not aware of our values and how they influence our actions, we may unknowingly sabotage our efforts to make changes in our lives. Or we may unconsciously force our value system on those around us, making their lives miserable and our own just as unhappy, because everyone doesn't live up to our expectations. We become codependent when we "need" other people to maintain our values in order to be happy.

In the following pages, we want you to look at your values as if you were using a camera. Bring them into focus. Consider the practice exercises as different angles from which to observe your values. Learn what the woman in the mirror really thinks.

Valuing self-care

One healthy value is that of taking care of ourselves. Being a woman today can mean being exhausted a lot of the time. Whether at home, in the workforce, or juggling both, "work" is never done—the list of things to do is never-ending.

Dr. Jo Ann Larsen, author of *I'm a Day Late and a Dollar Short . . . and It's OK*, responds:

"We are culturally programmed to be the caretakers of our families. In order to practice self-care, we must challenge the deeply ingrained—but erroneous—belief that constantly causes us to feel we are at fault when we can't accomplish everything. The flaw is in a culture that floods a caretaker at a multitude of levels with overwhelming messages about what she needs to do in order to be adequate. . . . Quite frankly, the busyness of care-taking is often a way of avoiding responsibility for who we are and what we need. We don't have to think. Or go on record. Or represent our needs or feelings to anyone. Or examine the substance of our life. Or take responsibility for our sense of self." (pp. 18–19, 26)

If we want to take care of ourselves, we must accept responsibility for establishing boundaries—healthy limits of what we can accomplish with our time, talents, and energy.

John Roger and Peter McWilliams offer sound advice to caretakers in their book, *You Can't Afford the Luxury of One Negative Thought*: "Service, as we define it here, is the art of taking such good care of yourself that you cannot help but take good care of others. When you fill yourself with love, happiness, and compassion, the desire to share the overflow of these with others is automatic. . . . Those who have given to others and found it depleting have not taken the time to give fully to themselves first. Always give to others of the overflow, and if you're giving to yourself unconditionally, the overflow will always be more than enough" (p. 257).

Finish the following sentences:

1. I am exhausted because

2. The scary thing for me about setting limits is

3. One thing I can do now to take care of myself is

Development of values

Our values develop from experiences and influences in many areas. These may be related to:
- basic needs—comfort, home, security, food and clothing
- family—lifestyle, structure, relationships
- culture—established "rules" for behavior
- peers—interests, pressures
- everyday life—home, community, school, work
- media—advertising, movies, T.V., news

List below fifteen values, ideas, or principles you recognize in your life, including those you wish were more of a priority. Then check (x) where these come from. Some may come from a combination of sources, so check all that apply.

Value	Basic Needs	Family	Culture	Peers	Everyday Life	Media
1.						
2.						
3.						
4.						
5.						
6.						
7.						
8.						
9.						
10.						
11.						
12.						
13.						
14.						
15.						

Identify your top five values in the spaces below. Then write a statement explaining why these values are important to you.

1._____

2._____

3._____

4._____

5._____

16

What opinions express values?

When we're busy taking care of everyone else, listening to everyone else, taking advice from everyone else, and absorbing other people's opinions about what's right for us, we can become fuzzy about our own opinions. We don't give ourselves credit or value for what *we* think. Codependents literally lose touch with who they are and what they think. To break out of this pattern, we must make the effort to rediscover what we value. Our opinions can give us clues about what's important to us. So explore some more.

Write your opinion about each category in the space provided. Then check in the columns on the right according to the following criteria:

> This idea or principle is *important*—it represents a value to me.
> This idea or principle involves a moral decision—*right or wrong*.
> This idea or principle is just a matter of *opinion*.

	your opinion	important	right or wrong	just opinion
Watching TV, movies				
Personal health				
Work				
Praise				
Doing things with people				
Independence				
Dependence				
Alone time				
Marriage				
Fidelity in marriage				
Drugs				
Reading				
Eating habits				
Cleaning your apartment/home				
Making money				
Family				
Children				
Education/Training				

Values and relationships

Give your own examples
of conflicting values:

We are usually attracted to people who like the same things we like. Then when we get to know them better—whether they be roommates, a spouse, or family members—individual differences become noticeable. Differences in our value systems is one reason relationships can be difficult to maintain.

Additional stress might be created when parents have adult children returning for a time (with or without their own children) to live at home or when adults find themselves caring for an elderly parent. Some people even find themselves sandwiched between parents *and* adult children.

Each of the following scenarios includes examples of differing and sometimes conflicting values.

1. After Kathy and Jeff got married, Kathy dropped out of school because she didn't think she needed a career if she was going to be a mother. Jeff was upset because he thought they would both graduate.

2. Raylene came back home to live while she finished college. Her parents were supportive. They assumed she would respect the family curfew and help out with her fair share of housework. Raylene felt that she was being treated like a little kid and was frustrated that she couldn't have friends stay as late as they wanted.

3. Tara saves money against future needs and emergencies. Her friend Melanie sees what she wants and buys it on credit.

4. Sally likes to come home to a quiet atmosphere, eat, read, and go to bed. Her roommate, Judy, likes to have friends in or go out to movies, parties, and museums.

5. Ben considers weeding the garden or painting a fence with his family a night out. His wife, Emily, considers these activities work and would rather walk along the beach for relaxation.

6. Edith lives with her son, Joshua, and daughter-in-law, Beth, and requires fairly constant attention. Edith gets angry with Beth when events are planned that exclude her. Beth is trying to manage her family and take care of Edith and feels frustrated in her efforts to please everyone.

Imposing or absorbing values

We may associate with or marry someone with values different from our own. These conflicting values may cause friction within our own family of parents and siblings. They can be a simple case of differing preferences, such as an early riser living with a night owl or one who is tidy and well organized living with another who is messy.

When it comes to absorbing values or imposing our values on others, there are two extremes that have negative consequences. The phrase "boundary issues" describes a primary characteristic of codependency. On the one hand, we may have no sense of our own boundaries. This means we have a difficult time defining where we end and other people begin. We have an unclear sense of self. Under these circumstances, we are out of touch with our own feelings and opinions; we can tell what everyone else's values are, but we are hard pressed to define our own.

On the other hand, we may see only one right way to think or do things—our way. When we insist on controlling other people with putdowns and criticism, and when our well-being is dependent on how closely others adhere to our value system, we are invading a roommate's, a spouse's, or family member's space in an unhealthy way.

When the beliefs and values of those around whom we live and with whom we associate are different than our own, it is easy to criticize in an attempt to feel better about ourselves. In design, contrast and diversity can combine to create a pleasing harmony. Contrast creates interest and variety. It is healthy to own our own values and let others own theirs. We become dysfunctional when we *need* other people to live by our values rather than simply wanting them to. Letting go of the need to impose our values on someone else is a sign of maturity.

* * *

If you are always complaining, angry, whining, or upset about the way others are "being" or "doing things," it's time to let go of insisting on your way.

OR

If you have absorbed others' opinions for so many years that you have no clue of what you personally value, it's time to set some boundaries and recognize your right to decide what's important to you.

* * *

Values I seek to impose on others:

Values I absorb from others:

Values I share in common with others:

19

Balancing values and life

Another principle of design that describes our lives is formal (symmetrical) and informal (asymmetrical) balance. We may wish for evenly spaced events or an equal measurement of time to devote to each area of our lives. Life rarely comes that way, however, and that's good. Although formal balance may be desirable in furniture and flower arrangements, life is much more engaging if it's a little off-kilter, so to speak.

When our children are small, for instance, they require intense amounts of our energy and attention. We may feel we are never getting anything else done. To balance, we may read in small doses, serve outside the home now and then, and work at other projects in small snatches of time. Likewise, involvement in a political campaign, pursuit of a educational degree, a job, or full-time care of a terminally ill relative may require a focus that puts other areas of our lives on hold. It may seem odd, but these kinds of things can actually make our lives more interesting.

Under each of the five categories listed below are some associated values. You may think of other values that are important to you because they affect your attitudes about things you are doing now.

Intellectual
- Seek opportunities for learning and growth.
- Read good books.
- Seek knowledge about the world and historical events.
- Identify and develop talents.

_____

_____

Spiritual
- Recognize and develop spiritual qualities.
- Accept individual worth.
- Develop moral courage.
- Believe in a supreme being.
- Accept responsibility for choices.

_____

_____

Physical
- Eat well-balanced meals.
- Exercise daily.
- Get regular dental checkups.
- Get enough sleep.
- Participate in a sport or activity you enjoy.

_____

_____

Emotional
- Be honest about feelings.
- Work through negative emotions and let go.
- Learn to forgive.
- Learn to nurture and care for yourself.

_____

_____

Social
- Recognize the healing power of doing good.
- Nurture others; give love and support.
- Strengthen family relationships.
- Encourage friends.
- Develop interpersonal and communication skills.

_____

_____

Planning for balance

Think about each area and write your own plan for balance, according to your values. You may want to write in letter form, in a list or chart, or you may illustrate your plan with pictures.

* * *

As you grow and have experiences in life, your perspective will change. As your circumstances change, some of your values will change also; others will remain constant.

Personal values that you have reflected on, identified, and internalized will serve as a unwavering standard for decisions you face at various stages of your life.

Discover yourself in all your complexity and diversity. This exploration—including this awareness of values—can be part of you throughout your life.

* * *

Additional Reading:

The Road Less Traveled
by M. Scott Peck

Family Histories

Bradshaw on the Family
by John Bradshaw

*I'm a Day Late and a Dollar
Short . . . and It's OK!*
by JoAnn Larsen

The Life of Christ
in the Four Gospels
of the New Testament

GIVING
NAMES TO
THOUGHTS,
FEELINGS,
AND WANTS

Profiles

Shannon grew up in a family where only positive emotions and expressions were allowed.

Lynette didn't believe it was OK for her to feel anger, so she held it in. She was always afraid she might explode one day.

Jan wanted to share with her boyfriend her thoughts about going to school but was afraid of his criticism.

When we are programmed to care for everyone else's feelings and wants, we can become out of touch with our own. This is a common symptom of codependency—being unaware of our own thoughts and feelings. Instead, we only know how others think and feel. Even though we cannot read minds, we make assumptions about what we think others expect from us. We keep busy anticipating their wants, agonizing over the past, and worrying about all that could possibly go wrong in the future. When we are angry or experience frustration, we smile anyway and say everything is fine. There just isn't time to deal with our feelings. Besides it's just too scary to figure those feelings out—especially because they are so negative.

If you are used to glossing over your feelings or ignoring them, this chapter will provide some simple and safe ways to begin looking at them. In this chapter, you will do exercises to help you identify your feelings and thoughts on a variety of topics and explore the importance of psychological safety when sharing thoughts and feelings. You will also practice changing some of your negative self-talk and bring some of your fears into the light to see what they really are.

As adults, there are things we fear—public speaking, decision making, intimacy, new jobs, heights, being in a large group of people, ending relationships, feelings of inadequacy, aging, or being alone. When we name thoughts and feelings (fears, wants, and frustrations, for example), it's like turning on the light—**they lose their power over us.** They cease to control us with discomfort and anxiety. Naming our thoughts and feelings is one of the most powerful concepts we can learn. Practice this skill throughout this chapter and learn the art of trusting yourself.

If it wasn't safe . . .

Perhaps we were raised in the typically codependent pattern of avoiding the honest expression of feelings and thoughts—even to ourselves. If we have spent most of our lives pleasing others and believing that what we think or feel is not important or may not be acceptable, it can be quite a chore to get a handle on exactly what *we* are feeling. If we haven't practiced being open, or don't feel it's OK or safe to express our feelings and opinions, our typical response if someone were to ask how we feel about something might be "I don't know."

Some people require only a few moments of reflection to reveal what is being felt inside. Others need a more active first step. It often helps to say something to ourselves (or others if they are involved):

" I'm upset, but I'm not sure why."

Or perhaps,

"Something feels wrong, but I can't put my finger on it."

Such a statement will begin an active search for the feeling you are sensing. You may be so far out of touch with your feelings that you have virtually forgotten what they mean. At this point it is still good to try to express yourself (Alberti, p. 64).

Another reason we avoid expressing frustrating thoughts and feelings is because we are socialized to "fix" everything that is out of place. We may be particularly uncomfortable with negative feelings, and our sensitive rescue antennae pick up these feelings as needing our expert repair immediately. In most cases, feelings don't need "fixing." They just need expression in a safe place:

"Oh, the blessing it is to have someone to whom we can speak fearlessly on any subject; one with whom one's deepest as well as one's most foolish thoughts come out simply and safely.

"Oh, the comfort, the inexpressible comfort of feeling safe with a person, having neither to weigh thoughts or measure words, but pouring them all right out just as they come, chaff and grain together, certain that a faithful hand will take them and sift them, keep what is worth keeping and then with a breath of kindness, blow the rest away."
—Dinah M. Craik

Exploring feelings

In her book *Minding the Body, Mending the Mind*, Dr. Joan Borysenko lists "three healthy attitudes toward feelings: (1) They are natural and human, (2) You are entitled to feel however you are feeling, whether or not the emotion is 'justified,' (3) Negative emotions are not bad. They are human. Most of the time they are appropriate. When someone you love dies, there is a time of sadness, grief, and mourning. If you don't allow yourself to experience the pain, it will crop up in other ways. If you get sick, the most natural response is to feel depressed. The natural reaction to hurt is anger. The only negative emotions are emotions that you will not allow yourself or someone else to experience and release" (pp. 161–163). One of the most essential steps in breaking out of codependency is to begin to recognize, accept, and appropriately express our true feelings.

It can be scary to move past the "I don't knows" in your life—or to express strong opinions other than "Whatever you say, dear." Below is a "feelings" chart to use in the following exercise. Practice identifying your feelings in some general categories before you move to more personal ones. Choose others besides the ones listed and write the first feeling or emotion you experience. Then in the second column, list more personal areas and/or questions you have strong feelings about—going back to school, having a baby, needing a car, working at a job you love, working at a job you hate, conflict in your family, moving, lack or abundance of financial support, etc.

FEELINGS WORD CHART

HAPPY	SAD	ANGRY	CONFUSED	SCARED	WEAK	STRONG	AWARE
amused	awful	aggravated	baffled	afraid	ashamed	bold	alert
cheerful	blue	annoyed	distracted	anxious	confused	brave	alive
delighted	crushed	critical	embarrassed	fearful	defenseless	capable	calm
ecstatic	depressed	disgusted	helpless	insecure	discouraged	confident	clear
excited	disappointed	enraged	lost	intimidated	exhausted	determined	concerned
glad	down	fed up	mixed up	nervous	fragile	energetic	content
optimistic	gloomy	frustrated	panicky	panicky	guilty	healthy	empathetic
pleased	hurt	furious	puzzled	shaky	ill	intense	loving
relaxed	miserable	irritated	surprised	tense	inadequate	open	passionate
relieved	painful	mad	trapped	terrified	overwhelmed	positive	secure
satisfied	terrible	outraged	troubled	timid	powerless	potent	sensitive
wonderful	unhappy	resentful	uncertain	vulnerable	run-down	powerful	warm

Source: Carkhuff, R.; Pierce, R.; Cannon, J. *The Art of Helping IV*. Amherst: Human Resource Development Press, 1980

GENERAL CATEGORY	HOW I FEEL ABOUT IT	SPECIFIC CATEGORY	HOW I FEEL ABOUT IT
Music			
Health			
Success			
Parenting			
Chocolate			
Money			

Feeling safe to share feelings

When we share our true feelings, we become vulnerable. To create an atmosphere of emotional safety, we must let go of evaluating, judging, and criticizing ourselves and others. Not letting go is a way to stay stuck and avoid our own growth. A focus on others' "wrong" feelings and thoughts (according to our opinions) is a sign of low self-esteem. Letting go means releasing ourselves and others from unrealistic expectations. We allow each other to *be*.

In her book *Making Contact,* Virginia Satir has identified the freedoms we need to grow and to know about ourselves. They are the foundation of emotional honesty and permission for full self-acceptance. Enormous personal power (self-awareness) results from such freedoms.

The Five Freedoms are—
1. The power to see and hear what is here and now.
2. The freedom to think what one thinks and to interpret.
3. The freedom to feel what one feels.
4. The freedom to choose, want, and desire.
5. The power to be creative through the use of imagination.

A statement by John Bradshaw clarifies:

"The Five Freedoms are opposed to any kind of perfectionistic system that measures through critical judgment, since judgment implies the measuring of a person's worth. Fully functional individuals have conflicts and differences of opinion but avoid judgment as a condition of another's worth. 'I am uncomfortable' is an expression of feeling. 'You are stupid, selfish, and crazy' is an *evaluative* statement" (p. 49).

1. Statements I make that are judgmental (about myself or others) include:

2. I feel safe expressing feelings and thoughts (where and with whom):

3. I can help others feel safe to express feelings and thoughts (dreams, worries, etc.) by:

27

Changing thoughts

Changing our thoughts begins with becoming aware of them. We can give in to the little voice inside of us that whispers doom, lack, and losing. It's this repetitive voice that makes *negative* assumptions about what is happening around us and what other people are thinking about us. This voice tells us we cannot change our lives or our thoughts, and that it's no use doing anything about it—we might just as well give up, grit our teeth, and endure our unhappiness.

For the next two minutes write down
all the thoughts going through your head.

After we become aware of our thoughts, the next step is to identify the payoffs—what we are willing to accept that reinforces our desire to stay stuck. Some of these might be more attention, special help, sympathy, or time off from school or work. This is tough because it requires emotional honesty. Changing thoughts also requires the acknowledgment of conscious alternatives. The magic fairy is not going to do this for us. We have to think and ponder and write alternatives that will work for us.

In the spaces below write down situations that prompt frustrating or negative thoughts. Identify your specific thought and the possible payoff (the negative reward). Then change the thought to a positive statement and anticipate a new payoff (a positive reward). Situations could include the death of a family member or close friend, marriage, divorce, money problems, personal or family failure, criticism, unemployment, etc.

SITUATION	THOUGHT	PAYOFFS	CHANGED THOUGHT	CHANGED PAYOFFS

Fears keep us from changing

Fears can keep us from changing, from trying something new, from growing. Fears, along with other negative thoughts, are obstacles to growth. You've probably heard yourself saying things like this once in a while:

> I'm a failure.
> I'm a helpless victim of circumstance.
> Nobody loves me.
> Everyone is judging me.

We can learn to let go of negative thoughts and feelings. We set our own limits, based on long-held concepts and decisions about ourselves. We will accomplish only that which we believe deep down is possible, according to our internal picture of ourselves (Alberti, p. 76–77).

In addition, we can choose how we talk to ourselves—what messages we give ourselves as we process information, sort out thoughts, and identify feelings. Change the following negative self-talk to positive messages. Include some of your own negative messages as you identify them.

NEGATIVE SELF-TALK	POSITIVE SELF-TALK
I'm stupid.	I make mistakes and that's OK.
I'm boring.	I am an interesting person.
I'm ugly.	I accept myself. I'm attractive.
I can't do anything right.	_____
I can't change.	_____
I'll never get . . .	_____
It's too late.	_____
No one understands.	_____
_____	_____
_____	_____
_____	_____
_____	_____

Additional Reading:

Your Perfect Right
by Robert E. Alberti
& Michael L. Emmons

*Minding the Body,
Mending the Mind*
by Joan Borysenko

*Feelings Buried Alive
Never Die*
by Karol Kuhn Truman

Making Contact
by Virginia Satir

As you become more aware of yourself, acknowledge your strengths as well as your weaknesses. Your wants are thoughts. Open up to the possibilities. Ask yourself what you are trying to satisfy in your life. Learn to accept your thoughts and feelings as a valid part of yourself—and give yourself permission to enjoy the five freedoms in your life.

REALITIES
AND MYTHS
OF GROWING UP

Profiles

Christine has been waiting for Mr. Right to come along for the past ten years since she got out of high school. She has been working as a file clerk in a small business for a small and static hourly wage with no benefits or retirement plan.

Marcy has had to work most of her married life just to help make ends meet. She will be happy when she can finally stay at home and be a mother.

Tanda is recently divorced after five years of marriage. "I'm devasted without Jim," she says. "He was my whole life."

Beth and her husband are finding the medical bills associated with removal of their nine-year-old daughter's brain tumor to be financially devastating. Beth is looking for a full-time job to help out, although she has no education or training.

As in the scenarios above, life will present us with a dose of reality in one way or another. And yet most people eventually land on their feet when presented with challenges or difficult circumstances. In this chapter we consider a few traps or myths that we easily fall prey to that keep us from making progress. We will look at control, happiness, fulfillment, effort, financial preparation, mistakes, and living in the present. If we are to make changes in our lives, the examination of our perceptions in these areas is essential in order for us to overcome codependency and take charge of our lives. We can analyze our own perceptions of reality, beginning with some definitions:

> *Reality is* things as they really are.
> *A Myth is* something imaginary.

Whether we see reality or myth depends on our perceptions.

> *Perceptions* are our *observations, judgments,* and
> *interpretations* about what happens to us.

Perceptions are the frame of reference through which we view the world; they create meaning in our lives. The same set of facts can look very different when viewed through someone else's eyes. Sometimes, because of experiences and circumstances, our perceptions may change.

Our perceptions

Here's a story about perceptions.

A woman was waiting in an airport for her flight home from London. She had bought an expensive package of foil-wrapped cookies to take home and had just settled into a seat to read her book until her flight was called. Just as she began reading, a gentleman sat down beside her and began to open the package of cookies. She watched in amazement as he put one in his mouth. Not to be outdone, she reached over and took one herself. And so they proceeded, silently eating the cookies one after another until only one was left. At this point the man broke the cookie in half and pushed one half toward her. She sat in silent outrage as he got up and left. Just then, her flight number was announced over the intercom; she reached for her ticket as she stood. There beneath her ticket was her unopened package of cookies. She had thought the gentleman to be extremely rude, when in reality he had been quite generous (Carol Shelton Walker, *Keynote address at UVCC Women's Conference.*).

Following are some examples of words that have meaning according to your perceptions of them. Try them out. See if you can discover a familiar phrase from each pictorial letter arrangement.

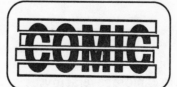 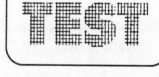

Life (of ease), (Spring) fever, (Screen) test, (All-star) game, (Rule of) thumb, (A maze-ing) grace, (Dead Sea) scrolls, Comic (strip), (Holy) mackerel   (by Charles Adkins, *Games*, 1979)

Myth or reality

We can look at myth and reality in much the same way. Look at the following phrases and determine which are myth and which are reality.

	MYTH	REALITY
1. Life will someday be easy.	MYTH	REALITY
2. I have total control over my life.	MYTH	REALITY
3. Someone else is always to blame for my problems.	MYTH	REALITY
4. There are multitudes of choices available.	MYTH	REALITY
5. It's someone else's job to make me happy.	MYTH	REALITY
6. I can create my life.	MYTH	REALITY
7. Getting things I want will make me happy.	MYTH	REALITY
8. If I get married, I'll never have to work.	MYTH	REALITY
9. If I'm good, nothing bad will ever happen to me.	MYTH	REALITY
10. For me to feel good about myself, I must be perfect.	MYTH	REALITY
11. It's OK for me to make mistakes.	MYTH	REALITY
12. I create my own happiness.	MYTH	REALITY
13. One person (or thing) can fill all my needs.	MYTH	REALITY
14. I will fall in love with the perfect person and live in harmony forever.	MYTH	REALITY

Myth #1, 3, 5, 7, 8, 9, 10, 13, 14
Reality #2, 4, 6, 11, 12

In the following activities we want to explore several myths within the context of reality—things as they really are.

Controlling your own life

In reality, each of us has total control over the quality of our own lives and problems—just as soon as we accept responsibility for our choices. For any number of reasons, we may consciously or unconsciously choose to stay with a lousy job, in a destructive relationship, or without a relationship. It is difficult to accept the fact that we are the cause of feelings that take away our happiness in life. We may not be the cause of all our bad experiences, yet we are the cause of our reactions to everything that happens to us.

When we take responsibility for our lives and our choices, we refuse to blame others for anything we are being, doing, or feeling. When we understand that no one else creates what goes on in our lives, we will be in control.

On the other hand, it's easier to play the victim role and assume that everyone or everything else is responsible for our happiness. Many women still expect the men in their lives to "make them happy." In the space below, write a list of what you have control over in your life and what things you have no control over. If you are wondering how to decide, Dr. Jo Ann Larsen suggests that when you want to blame someone else, simply ask yourself,

> "What am I not doing in my life that I could be doing that
> I am blaming (him, them) for not doing for me?"

Things I have control over in my life:
-
-
-
-
-
-
-

Things I have no control over:
- The weather
- Other people's behavior
-
-
-
-

Creating your own happiness

How do you create positive circumstances that will bring good feelings to you? Consider these possibilities:

1. *Dwell on your successes* instead of your failures.

2. *Notice the good* things you're doing and the pleasures you do have in your life.

3. *Do something that makes you feel good.* Everyone needs breaks from the ordinary routines in life.

4. *Quit complaining* about the things you're not getting from others. No one likes to be around a complainer.

5. *"Don't wait—initiate"* — when there are things you want.

It's possible in the course of life to have one area become your total focus: work, children, or a relationship, for instance. But when that one thing is gone, you are left with nothing. When your happiness depends on only one thing in your life, negative side effects accompany the emotional dependency. It's easy to become protective and controlling rather than expansive and giving.

Let's examine a relationship, for example. When we depend on just a relationship for fulfillment, life looks like this:

```
┌─────────────────────────────┐
│                             │
│       RELATIONSHIP          │
│                             │
└─────────────────────────────┘
```

When the relationship disappears, life suddenly looks like this:

```
┌─────────────────────────────┐
│                             │
│                             │
│                             │
└─────────────────────────────┘
```

A whole life

In her book *Feel the Fear and Do It Anyway*, Susan Jeffers suggests an alternate way of handling your life. She suggests a process of helping you release desperation, emptiness, and fear. The following whole-life grid looks different from the relationship (or children or work) box on the opposite page (pp. 138-139).

CONTRIBUTIONS SERVICE	FAMILY	WORK
HOBBY	ALONE TIME	RELATIONSHIP
FRIENDS	LEISURE	PERSONAL GROWTH

Take some time to think about what components you would like to include in your life and fill in the boxes. Shut your eyes and visualize what you would like that part of your life to look like. Then write down what your mind created for you, paying attention to detail.

Life always takes effort

Once we get our bodies in shape, we can't stop working out or our muscles will start losing tone within an amazingly short time. We must keep at it. The intellect acts in the same way. When problem solving, stimulating discussion, or reading is part of our daily lives, our minds are sharp. However, it is easy to get in a "comfort zone" with our bodies, our minds, and our lives and just coast along—waiting for someone else to do the work.

Answer the following questions:

1. What in my life do I want to be easy?

2. What do I want that will take effort?

3. What takes effort that I never thought would be hard?

4. What are areas in my life that could use more effort?

Economic Reality

An additional reality of today whether we are married or single is that we will probably work at least twenty-six years of our lives for economic reasons. For example, 50 percent of women will be the main breadwinner before they reach retirement age. For some, economic reality hits during a divorce when an average woman's income drops dramatically even with child support. For others, this economic reality comes when a husband dies, becomes disabled, or loses his job, or a child's serious health problem requires expensive medical treatment. Someone who says "It will never happen to me" usually finds out too late that life offers many challenges, including financial challenges, without warning. However, facing these possibilities and being prepared can reduce the fear or distress of having to support oneself.

Identifying the costs

1. Identify how much it would cost to support yourself for one year.

    housing   _____
    home maintenance   _____
    food   _____
    transportation   _____
    insurance (medical, life, car) _____
    entertainment   _____
    education   _____
    clothing   _____
    taxes   _____
    contributions
                Total   _____

2. If you have children, add to your expenses the cost of supporting them.

    food   _____
    housing   _____
    education   _____
    clothing   _____
    medical   _____
                Total   _____

3. How long could you support youself at age fifty with $20,000 worth of life insurance?

4. How much would you earn at minimum wage?
    (This means you would be earning how much yearly?)

5. How much would you need to earn per hour to meet your estimated cost of living?

Making mistakes is OK

Life is a learning process. Each crisis we encounter requires stretching and changing and growing. In the process of growing, we will make mistakes. It is actually to our benefit that we make those mistakes, for it is from our errors that much of our learning takes place. Dr. Jo Ann Larsen suggests "that we have a right—in the process of becoming—to make mistakes. In that process, we must remember that our *growth* needs to be separated from our *worth*. As human beings, we are valuable simply because we *are*. When we confuse our *growth* with our *worth*, and then make mistakes, we devalue ourselves.

"Recognize that a mistake may only be a decision based on the best information you had at the time. And you are not making a 'mistake' when another person has an opinion about what you 'ought' to do differently. That simply is another person's opinion. Give yourself permission to make mistakes without beating yourself up inside. Instruct yourself to face your mistakes, learn from them, and then lay them to rest. And then give yourself credit when you see your growth" (pp. 125–27).

Listen to your own internal dialogue to see if you're making negative statements like these:

- Anything less than perfect is not acceptable.
- I can't make a mistake.
- I've blown it.
- I never do anything right.
- There's something wrong with me.

Identify some of your own unrealistic expectations and negative statements:

-

-

-

-

-

Living in the now

As we go through life, we often focus on the destination. We tell ourselves that on a certain day at a certain hour we will pull into the station of happiness. Then wonderful dreams will come true. How anxiously we await the end of our journey: "When I'm eighteen..." "When I buy my dream car or home..." "When I get married..." "When the kids are all in school..." "When I put the last kid through college..." "When I retire..." "then I'll live happily ever after."

The station is only a dream that constantly outdistances us. *The true joy of life is the trip.* Celebrate the things happening now: enjoy the butterfly, embrace the snow, run with the ocean, delight in the trees. Celebrate by embracing your pain as well as your joys. What most of us do not realize is that pain and joy run together. When we cut ourselves off from our pain, we have cut ourselves off from joy as well. Live in the now, with all its problems and its agonies, its joy and its pain. It means you're alive. For most of us there is some beauty around us day by day. We sit beside it or look past it or ignore it. We fail to let it speak to our spirits, to call out the beauty within us. We are somewhere else, living for tomorrow, or fretting over the past.

What are my present joys?

What are my present sources of pain?

What can I do to live in the "now?"

Self-discovery is sometimes difficult, yet it's almost always rewarding. Continue the process through each chapter. Some information you seek will come easily to your mind. Other parts of you will take time to uncover. Love yourself during the whole process.

"Relish the moment" is a good motto, especially when coupled with a verse of scripture

"This is the day which the Lord hath made; we will rejoice and be glad in it."
Psalm 118:24

Stop waiting anxiously for everything to happen right so you will be happy.

Instead, *climb more mountains, eat more ice cream, go barefoot more often, watch more sunsets, laugh more.*

Live life as you go along.

Additional Reading
Feel the Fear and Do It Anyway
by
Susan Jeffers

RECOGNIZING
THE INNER SELF

The inner self

In several of her books, Madeleine L'Engle has her characters consider the question: "When are you the most you?" Meg, for instance, is most Meg when she's doing math (*A Wind in the Door*, pp. 104, 114). Vicky is most Vicky when she's not thinking consciously about herself (*Ring of Endless Light*, pp. 166-167).

In another passage with Vicky: "I let my mind drift toward the dolphins, . . . my breathing quieted, slowed, moved to the gentle rhythm of the sea. The tenseness left my body until it seemed that the rock on which I sat was not embedded deep in the sand but was floating on quiet waters. My mind stopped its running around like a squirrel on a wheel, and let go. I sat there and I didn't think. I was just being. And it felt good" (pp. 225-226).

"Beyond identities and desires there is an inner core of self. Although we are born with a pure self-concept, we begin immediately to set up defense systems to protect ourselves. Gradually we develop a 'world self-concept,' shaped by the treatment we receive from those around us. As we grow up we accept this 'world' self in place of our Inner Self, and measure our worth by other people's opinions, our appearance, social achievements, and so on. Over time we may become totally unconscious of our own true feelings, needs, and wants" (*Ellsworth*, p. 23). We have discussed this condition as symptomatic of codependency. Even so, we can peel back the layers and learn to recognize the voice of our Inner Self.

* * *

To those who listen, it speaks assurance and direction constantly and without fail. Its nature is peaceful, its expression is thought, and its action is unconditional love.

* * *

When we operate from this Inner Self, we are self-aware and abundant—overflowing in fact. Our fears automatically disappear. In this chapter we will look at attributes and practices that bring us in touch with that Inner Self—that part of us that accepts us fully and unconditionally: being, breathing, affirming, nurturing, giving, and connecting. These skills help us become inwardly focused and less inclined to control others because we feel more in control of our own lives.

Being the most you

A way to become aware of your Inner Self is to remember times when you were being the most you. Some possibilities to get you started thinking include: dancing, hiking, sitting still, writing, playing an instrument, singing, sharing thoughts, helping someone, working or playing with a child, etc.

I am most me when . . .

WHEN I AM TUNED INTO MY "WORLD" SELF, I—	WHEN I AM TUNED INTO MY INNER SELF, I—
try to control	trust, I let go
don't notice my blessings	appreciate
have insatiable needs	love
am insensitive	care
am in turmoil	am at peace
am blocked	am creative
don't know I count	count
repel	attract
make a negative difference	make a positive difference
take	give and receive
am bored	am involved
am filled with self-doubt	am confident
am dissatisfied	am content
wait and wait	live now
never enjoy	am joyful
hold resentment	forgive
am tense	relax
am poor	have so much
am lonely	am connected

(Adapted from *Feel the Fear and Do It Anyway* by Susan Jeffers, p. 210.)

Breathing

Write what you imagined
while you were relaxed:

Why talk about breathing? It's something we do automatically. One way to quiet our minds and tune into the Inner Self is to get back to basic breathing and relaxing. Following is an exercise from *Creative Visualization* by Shakti Gawain:

> Get in a comfortable position, either sitting or lying down, in a quiet place where you won't be disturbed. Relax your body completely. Starting with your toes and moving up to your scalp, think of relaxing each muscle in turn, letting all tension flow out of your body. Breathe deeply and slowly, from your abdomen. Count down slowly from ten to one, feeling yourself getting more and more deeply relaxed with each count.

> When you feel deeply relaxed, start to imagine something you want exactly as you would like it. If it is an object, imagine yourself with the object, using it, enjoying it, showing it to friends. If it's a situation or event, imagine yourself there and everything happening just as you want it to. Imagine any detail that makes it more real to you (p. 9).

When you become more aware of your breathing and relaxing, you will also begin to notice when you momentarily quit breathing—when you're angry, upset, confused, hurt, or frightened, for instance.

This is what happens to my breathing and relaxing when I am angry, confused, hurt, or frightened:

Affirming

Society emphasizes the negative things that happen around us. It is just as realistic, though, to think about the positive things. An *affirmation* is a positive, present-tense statement that something is already so. It can be general or specific. Here are a few ideas:

Every day I'm getting better and better.

I'm a radiant being, filled with light and love.

I'm OK and I like myself.

I am a child of God.

I accept my feelings as part of myself.

I am attracting loving relationships into my life.

I love my work and am rewarded creatively and financially.

I have enough time, energy, and money to accomplish my desires.

I am taking care of myself.

Affirmations connect us with our Inner Self. If these concepts are new to you, it will take time to get used to them. Remember the following as you develop your own affirmations:

1. Phrase them in present tense. It's important to state them as if they already exist.
2. Affirm what you do want, not what you don't want.
3. Short and simple affirmations are more effective.
4. Always choose affirmations that feel totally right for you.

While you are stating these affirmations, relax your body. If you continue to feed yourself these affirming words long enough, you will eventually notice a warm calm come over your body and your mind, and you will feel safe (Gawain, pp. 21–25).

Write some of your own affirmations here:

1.

2.

3.

4.

Nurturing

To nurture is to care. Too much of the time, we're so busy caring for others, we neglect our own needs. Taking care of our own needs is not being self-centered, (which means taking care of yourself to the exclusion of others), but as Dr. Jo Ann Larsen suggests "being centered *in* self. It means gathering current and accurate information about yourself at any one moment" (p. 23–24) and acting from an inner center of peace for your own well-being.

Nurturing means we initiate opportunities and experiences that fill and make us feel complete rather than wait for someone else to make us happy. It is being free to know ourselves, to be ourselves in the process of becoming.

Many of us do not know ourselves well because we are constantly scanning the responses of others to determine how we are coming across. Instead of looking inward and questioning, "What do I think, feel, or want?" we look outward for the signals of others to tell us whether we are acting appropriately and according to their expectations. If we nurture ourselves appropriately, we will develop inner strength and peace. It is just as important and every bit as worthy of our time to nurture *ourselves* as it is to nurture any of God's other children.

What are nurturing things I do for myself?

What are nurturing things I *want* to do for myself?

Giving

Do you think of yourself as a giving person? Often we give as an exchange, "You do this for me and I'll do this for you."

This kind of thinking sets up a need to control others so we won't feel shortchanged, and creates resentment. Why do we find it so difficult to give? First, it requires maturity. Second, giving is an acquired skill that few of us have mastered. The reason most of us have never practiced these skills is simple—it usually never occurs to us that we aren't behaving like adults or that we aren't giving (Susan Jeffers, p. 169).

If we are constantly expecting, we will be disappointed that the world isn't treating us right.

A BEGINNING PLACE TO START GIVING
MY LIST OF PEOPLE TO THANK AND WHEN I DID IT:

- Think about people in your life now and significant ones in your past.
- List ways they have contributed to your life in their own special way (*even if they brought you pain*).
- *Now* thank them.

PERSON	CONTRIBUTION	DATE THANKED

More to giving

You can also learn to give other things: *Think of other things to add to the list:*

- praise

- time

- love

-

-

-

-

Understand that giving is about outflow. It is about letting go of our crouched, withholding self and standing tall with outstretched arms.

> Like any other skill,
> giving takes practice.

Barbara Sher comments: "Some people still feel comfortable and comforted talking to God. Since religion has lost its central place in our lives, many of us don't have this source of comfort any more. It's too bad because it was such a good one" (p. 103).

We can choose to reinstate this source of comfort in our lives if we have lost it. Religion can have any place in our lives that we choose it to have. We don't have to be negatively affected by our society.

Susan Jeffers states: "I believe that what all of us are really searching for is this divine essence within ourselves. If we do not consciously and consistently focus on the spiritual part of ourselves, we will never experience the kind of joy, satisfaction, and connectedness we are all seeking" (p. 202).

Connecting

Recreate your whole life grid from chapter four. Let one of your permanent boxes be the Inner Self. Each day incorporate time to be quiet and focus on the Inner Self, using books, scriptures, affirmations, inspirational tapes, meditation, prayer, or whatever works for you. The positive, loving energy that flows from this spiritual connection will spill over into every area of your life.

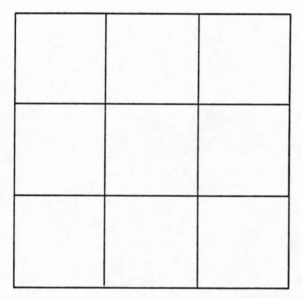

Connecting, affirming, breathing, nurturing, giving, being—all are ideas that may be new to you as you make contact with your Inner Self. They are skills you can practice that say you like yourself and are of great worth. You may choose greater abundance in your life at any point. The past five chapters have been compiled to help you

**discover yourself and accept that
you are loving and capable.**

Additional Reading:

Creative Visualization
by Shakti Gawain

Getting to Know the Real You
by Sterling Ellsworth
& Richard Ellsworth

*A Circle of Quiet &
Ring of Endless Light*
by Madeleine L'Engle

WHY GOOD WOMEN ARE UNHAPPY LIVING WITH GOOD MEN

(AND VICE-VERSA)

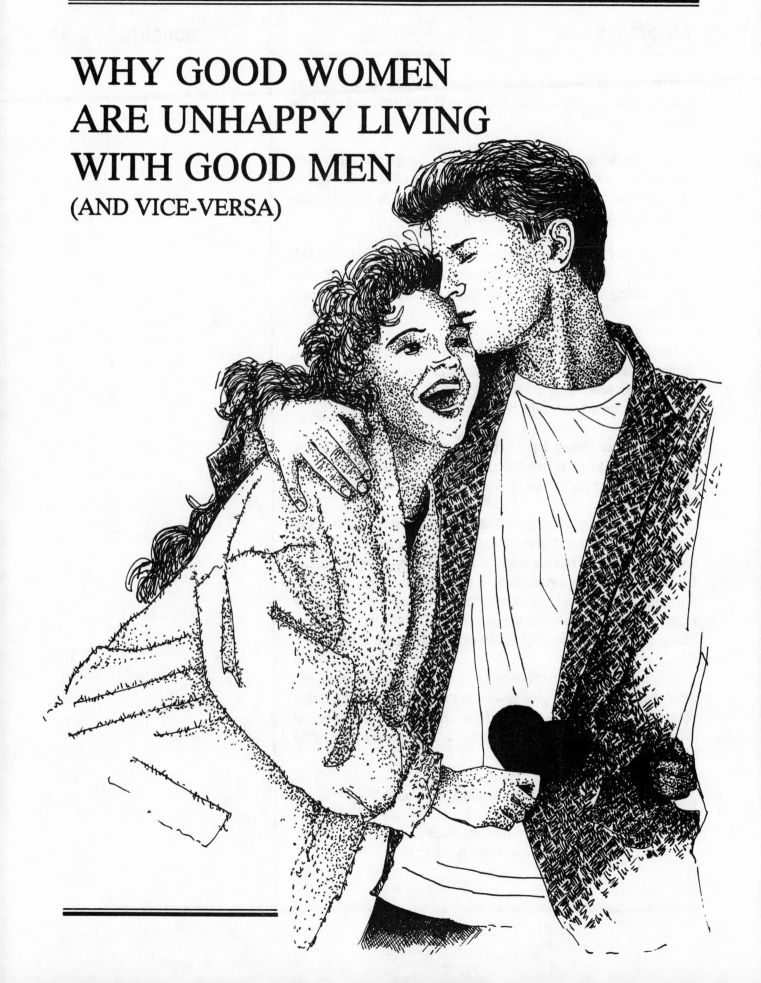

Profiles

Tom and Janette can't seem to break the argument cycle. They disagree with and criticize each other as if they were angry all the time.

Annie is disappointed when *Tim* doesn't jump in and help with the housework when he comes home from the office. "Doesn't he know I've been working hard, too?" she thinks to herself. Her unexpressed expectations cause frustration for both.

Evelyn and Bill have been married for forty-five years and Bill has recently retired. He is constantly underfoot and follows Evelyn around telling her what to do in the home that has been her domain for years.

Matt and Carol rarely disagree because Matt rarely expresses his opinion. Carol insists on having things her way and goes into a frenzy when something unexpected comes up. Matt is easygoing and doesn't want to rock the boat.

Georgia and Randy have been going together for five years. Georgia wants to get married; Randy is afraid of the commitment. Having a partner for weekend events suits him just fine.

A relationship, according to Webster, defines some sort of connection, mutual interest, or involvement with another person. There are various types of relationships in our society: with a girl- or boyfriend, neighbor, employer, relative, or marriage partner. The relationship may be formal or informal, healthy or unhealthy. It may be maintained with occasional contact or require constant attention. The kind we'll consider here involves a boyfriend or husband.

The clearer you can get about what you want to have happen and what you are willing to give and be in the relationship, the richer your experience will be. This information is for your *personal evaluation, not to be used in judgment of another person*. One of the best lessons you can learn is that—

The only person you can change is yourself—
and when things seem frustrating in a
relationship the best place for
your focus is
you.

Accepting differences

In her newspaper column, Dr. Jo Ann Larsen explores differences in relationships. A relationship starts out with birds singing and sighs of contentment. Two people, dazzled by the glow of romance, idealize the image of the other, each convinced that he or she has found the perfect mate. All too soon, though, they begin seeing the differences.

> "He's so messy. I don't know why it's so hard for him to pick up after himself. He leaves everything lying around. It just infuriates me."
> —Wife

> "I can't believe how meticulous she is. And how impatient. I'd pick up my things if she would just wait, but I can't even put something down without her whisking it off to some cupboard or drawer. Then she just freaks out and complains and complains about how terrible I am for not putting my clothes away. She gets downright nasty."
> —Husband

The romance has faded. Two disillusioned people, now seeing only the faults and flaws, deal with their very real differences—destructively. If you find yourself making harsh judgments because your mate didn't turn out to be the way you expected, take heed. If you find yourself manipulating or controlling with sulkiness or pouting or the silent treatment, you are using codependent behavior patterns. Following are several ways to deal constructively with differences.

1. Accept your partner's right to be different.

Each of us has a different view of the world that comes from our background and experiences. We have the right to be ourselves, the person we are, the sum total of our feelings, thoughts, behaviors, tastes, dislikes, opinions, and perceptions. Many of the things we complain about may simply reflect our own preferences, values, or individual habits and lifestyle—not an absolute standard.

> There is no *right* way to dress, eat, make a bed, clean a sink, or scramble eggs.

Differences cont.

2. Allow for mistakes.

Letting other people make mistakes without penalty is difficult but so important. Usually when we are having a problem with someone else's way of doing things, it's because we expect perfection—and perfection means doing things *our* way. Everyone needs the right to be wrong and the right to grow from his or her mistakes—without another's judgment. Let it be all right if your partner forgets to run your errand or wash the dishes, or if he invites friends over without checking with you first.

3. Learn to let go of the frustration—learn to accommodate.

Assess your level of frustration by answering the following questions as honestly as you can:

1. When I listen to myself, do I hear a constant stream of negative remarks—sarcasm, doubts, rebuffs, putdowns?

2. Does my tone get harsher when I'm disappointed or hurt?

3. Can I distinguish between a mountain and a molehill?

4. Do I respect differences in preferences and values, or do I insist that I have the only right standard?

5. Do I hang on to frustration, disappointment, and unmet expectations?

6. What are the positive things I notice about our differences?

7. What are things my partner does that are easy to accept?

8. What are things my partner does that are hard to accept?

9. How can *I* change?

Changing yourself

When a relationship begins, it's easy to say,

> **"I'll adapt."**
> **"Those idiosyncrasies won't bother me."**

Then when they do bother us, the tune changes to,

> **"If he would only . . ."**

A relationship suffers from neglect because both people are waiting for the other to change. After all, each person thinks,

> **"It's your fault we're having difficulty."**
> **"You're the one who needs to change."**
> **" I'll just wait until you take care of the problem."**

Whether you are in a relationship or not, there are things you can work on. Look over the list below.

When I focus on myself, these are things I see that I want to change (check all that apply):
  —saying "thank you" more often
  —being more courteous
  —giving more compliments
  —being more affectionate
  —saying "I love you"
  —avoiding criticism
  —making time to do fun things together
  —balancing the checkbook
  —avoiding name-calling, e.g., "stupid," "lazy," "slob"
  —staying within the budget
  —helping more with the children
  —picking up after myself
  —controlling or preventing anger over little things
  —being on time or calling if I'm late
  —sticking to issues when we disagree
  —being willing to do my share at home
  —letting go of past hurts
  —expressing appreciation at the moment

Avoiding control traps

Sometimes we may try to force another person to conform to our point of view or our standard. Essentially, the message is:

"Do what I want, or I will hate you, leave you, punish you, judge you, or ignore you."

To de-control your relationship, try these strategies:

1. Avoid absolutes such as **always** and **never.**

2. Avoid the words **should, ought, must,** and **have to.**

3. Give up threats, orders, blaming, criticism, sarcasm, judging, and any other form of communication that functions to pressure your partner to fall in line—*your* line.

4. Give up labeling your partner as insensitive, disorganized, talkative, practical or impractical, flighty, selfish, stupid, too sensitive or insensitive, etc. We all have internal measuring standards by which we assess the behavior, opinions, and ideas of others. Our standards do not measure what is real at all—they only reflect what we know, what we have experienced, or what we are comfortable with.

5. Use opinion language. Instead of taking the position **"You are wrong"** or **"That's not true!"** let your awareness of your own feelings and thoughts be reflected in your language. For example, **"Here's how I see the issue." "I respect your opinion."**

Situations where I didn't use opinion language:	Situations where I have used absolutes:
Situations where I have used labels:	**Situations where I use communication as a pressure:**

Infidelity poisons love

When a relationship settles in, the wear and tear of everyday stress begins. Couples focus so much of their time and energy on the practical things they can lose touch with each other. Three myths plague many modern marriages:

1) *The marriage will take care of itself.*

It won't. Marriage is a dynamic interaction between two growing, changing people, and it requires constant attention to be close and meaningful. Maintaining commitments requires effort.

2) *If the marriage is not successful, I should start over.*

By definition, marriage is a *process*. Consequently, it will be more successful at some points than at others. Many people want or expect instant success in all dimensions of marriage; if any aspect seems less than perfect, one can despair and think, "I married the wrong person." This attitude frequently turns one's attention toward someone other than the marriage partner.

3) *Loving my spouse means I can safely become involved with someone else.*

"The task for every married person is to maintain loyalty and fidelity with one person—the spouse. It is inappropriate to feel and express to others the same feelings of love one expresses to a spouse.

"Fidelity in marriage is measured by the degree of loyalty, allegiance, and commitment between husband and wife. Two souls united in matrimony can achieve spiritual and temporal unity only if they constantly increase their friendship, love, and loyalty by expressing feelings verbally, maintaining mutual respect, and demonstrating concern for each other. When we respect our marriage vows, we feel comfortable with ourselves. We don't have to worry about covering our tracks. If we act dishonestly, though, we find no peace" (Smith, pp. 59–61).

When we harbor codependent behavior patterns and wish to avoid responsibility for what is happening in our lives, we can easily blame our partners when things go wrong. It takes courage and emotional honesty to look at our own actions and determine what changes *we* can make.

Mutual self-discovery

The following are statements that can encourage mutual self-discovery. Using these statements, you can either report on your own feelings or you can ask the same of your partner. Decide how you would like to use this information to enhance your closeness. Respect each other's answers, make it safe for each other to be completely honest, and create a loving and understanding atmosphere for any sharing you do.

1. A positive word describing our relationship is _____

2. One way we are alike (or different) is _____

3. One of the most fun things we ever did was _____

4. The needs you satisfy in me are _____

5. Needs of mine I would enjoy your satisfying are _____

6. A song that reminds me of you is _____

7. One of your greatest assets is _____

8. One thing I treasure having learned from you is _____

9. You are the most helpful when _____

10. A habit of mine that bothers me most is _____

11. When I don't want to answer questions, I _____

12. Something that is helping us to grow closer is _____

13. To keep from being hurt, I _____

14. An important issue between us right now is _____

15. I wish you would let me know when I _____

16. I feel especially loved when you _____

17. One way I try to show my love for you is _____

18. One of my greatest fears is _____

19. In the future, I would like our relationship to become more _____

Marriage—event or lifestyle?

When we are teenagers (and beyond), our thoughts of the future usually include a wedding somewhere along the way. We imagine the event—a beautiful dress, a handsome groom, relatives and friends smiling their approval, gifts, and warm feelings. We dream about and prepare for the *event* of marriage, but may not spend much time thinking about the *relationship* and *responsibilities* of marriage after the event. We use the Cinderella phrase, "I'll live happily ever after . . ." and we assume that the relationship will be perfect. It's another story (and no fairytale!) to realize that after saying "I do" comes the challenging work. Lots of it.

In the space below, jot down any notes you want to remember or imagine about the wedding "event."

For a minute, close your eyes and imagine—(or remember)

The bridal showers

Choosing and mailing the announcements

Taking pictures

Finding a wedding dress

Choosing colors and bridesmaids

Picking a date

Selecting flowers

Finding the perfect ring

The lifestyle after the event . . .

Now think past the event to the relationship you want to build with a mate *or* the relationship you have now that you want to enhance. Consider the following questions:

1. How easy is it for me to accept people who are different than those in my original family?

2. What opportunities have I had in the past to practice tolerance?

3. Building a relationship of trust requires time together sharing thoughts and feelings. Emotional intimacy is as important as physical intimacy. What is important to me to understand about emotional and physical intimacy?

4. How easy is it for me to compromise, resolve concerns, give and take?

5. What experiences have I had in the past that have taught me to compromise, resolve concerns, give and take?

6. How would I handle a particularly stressful situation where there might be a difference of opinion or hurt feelings?

7. How would I reach out to my partner?

8. How would I express feelings of anger?

9. What have I done in the past in such situations?

Keeping love alive

All couples hurt and disappoint each other at times. One of two things then happens: either we forgive *or* we slowly accumulate resentment.

For love to last we must be able to forgive. Simply shelving our feelings or putting them out of mind is not forgiveness. Nor is explaining away the other person's behavior.

Forgiving is a genuine, voluntary release of anger and hurt. And it is necessary in order for a relationship to flourish again.

In the final analysis, the most important rule of love is this: Toward both your partner and yourself behave only in ways that enhance your own self-worth, dignity, and integrity.

When you feel good about yourself, you possess the confidence and personal contentment necessary for love to remain truly alive.

The sentiment above comes from Jo Ann Larsen's newspaper column. Perhaps you are unhappy living with a spouse (or frustrated in a potential relationship), complaining and sighing that your expectations have turned to disappointment. If you want to see change, look inward and accept yourself, allow for differences and mistakes, and figure out one thing you will do personally to make a difference in the relationship. It is your choice.

Additional Reading:

Couples
by Carlfred Broderick

Living, Loving, and Learning
by Leo Buscaglia

Angle of Repose
by Wallace Stegner

WHERE DO I
FIT A BABY
IN MY LIFE?

Mattie, a mother of five, remarks, "My first child was so wonderful and I loved her so much that I wondered if I would have any love left over for another child. I have found, though, that each child has brought a greater measure of love into our family."

Joan, an unmarried teenager, explains, "As much as I love my baby, I wish I had waited until I was older and married. My boyfriend said he loved me and to trust him, but he broke off our relationship when he found out I was pregnant."

Rita, age thirty-eight and expecting her first, exclaims, "I wondered if I would ever marry and have children! Now I'm really going to have a baby. I'm so awed by the whole process."

Stephanie, a young married woman who found out after two miscarriages that she is unable to have children, shares this thought: "I am working through my grief and hope we can adopt. If not, I will find other ways to be involved with children."

Ellen, mother of a handicapped child, states, "It was hard for me at first to believe that my child was born blind. It's so challenging at times that I wonder how I keep going, but each little step of progress seems like a wondrous miracle."

One of the realities for most women is bearing and raising children. From the profiles above, though, we can see a variety of circumstances that will affect having and caring for children. In addition, as our children have children and we become grandmothers, we face a whole new set of decisions and challenges.

In this chapter, look at the part that children and grandchildren play or will play in your life. The sections in this chapter include choosing to have children, identifying your feelings about that choice and the power to create life, becoming a mother/grandmother, and seeing the complete picture. As a grandmother, you will find it important to assess the involvement and time commitment you will make to your grandchildren. If unrealistic assumptions are made about your availability to care for grandchildren, the result could be unproductive guilt and resentment.

Facing choices

We make choices every day, like what color of clothes we will wear, what toothpaste we will use, whether or not to wear a coat, what to eat for breakfast, and so on.

We make moral choices also. For example, we choose whether or not to hurt someone, to cheat on a test, to avoid drugs, to help someone who is being teased, to lie about where we have been, or to take something from someone else without asking.

We live in a society whose moral standards are declining. This change has eroded much of the public support and many of the natural social barriers that traditionally discouraged people from participating in premarital (or extramarital) sexual activity. Society no longer considers sexual intimacy a privilege of marriage but has reduced it to an act of pleasure to be engaged in at will. Society would have us believe such behavior brings with it no permanent consequences, encouraging an ever-decreasing acceptance of personal responsibility.

As human beings, we have an intuitive understanding of moral choices. Deep inside we can feel what is right and what is wrong. **We can know that we are going against our own moral judgment and making a bad choice,** especially if we are secretive and do not want to tell family members or a close friend. Sometimes bad decisions are made in a split second because of peer pressure or deep insecurity; at other times we think about them and are uncomfortable with the decision for a long time before anything happens. Such decisions are void of any integrity or love—for oneself or others—because the consequences are negative for all involved. Without integrity (complete honesty) or love, it is impossible to build a sense of self-worth.

Another way we can recognize when we are going against our own moral judgment or when we aren't doing what we feel is right is that we keep explaining and justifying what we think should be—

> "It's OK. Everybody does it."
>
> "No one will know or care."
>
> "Just this once won't hurt."
>
> "I'm only hurting myself."
>
> "We're really in love, so that makes it right."

Feelings about moral choices

Identify your feelings about moral choices by thoughtfully considering your answers to the following questions:

1. Who are safe people for me to talk with about questions, feelings, decisions, and concerns I am facing?

2. What are situations I might find myself in where I have choices to make that I'm not sure about?

3. How did I feel after making a choice that compromised my values?

4. How do I make myself feel better when I'm making a choice I don't feel comfortable with?

5. What decisions have I made lately that built my self-worth?

6. What are some questions I need answers to before I get in high-pressure situations?

The power to create

It is through the power to create life that a man and woman become parents. Within a family children are prepared for the responsibilities of adult life. From early teenage years, young women develop the physical capacity to have children, yet the teenage years may not be the best time to have a baby. And becoming sexually active before marriage can dramatically affect a woman's life. Having a baby at this age can put an end to school, reduce self-esteem, and thwart the process of self-discovery.

Most specialists say that a loving family starts with a loving marriage; the family is a byproduct of the relationship between husband and wife. The most appropriate time to fit a baby in your life, then, is *after* marriage. This gives the child a sense of identity. When a child senses his parents' love, he feels secure.

In order to understand your own feelings about this power to create life, complete the following sentences:

1. Raising a family

2. Being a mother/grandmother

3. Marriage is

4. My mother

5. A pregnant woman

6. A woman's body

7. A baby is

8. A woman feels good when

9. When I am with my boyfriend/husband

10. I am uncertain about

11. I would like to know more about

Physical and emotional commitment

Becoming a mother means more than simply creating offspring. It requires physical and emotional commitment, which includes—

> **nurturing** a child
>
> **protecting** a child
>
> **caring** for a child
>
> **teaching** a child
>
> **disciplining** a child
>
> **helping** a child
>
> **encouraging** a child
>
> **feeding** a child
>
> **providing** for a child
>
> **giving** time and energy to a child
>
> (*even when we're exhausted, ill, or angry*)

Mothering is the hardest and most rewarding work in life. That's why commitment is vital and why it's important to *choose* motherhood when you can love and care for your baby responsibly. Too often young women get pregnant because they are sad, lonely, or angry.

Write in as much detail as possible your response to the two questions* below :

1. If I were to be born tomorrow, under what circumstances would I want to be born?

2. If I were going to give birth tomorrow, under what circumstances would I want to bring this child into the world?

*From *Aanchor Curriculum* by Terry Olson

Seeing the complete picture

We see pink or blue booties, darling little dresses and sleepers; we hear gooing and cooing; we think how wonderful it would be to have a little one to care for. It's best to build a *complete* picture of what having a baby entails, however. Usually when we dream of babies, the details take care of themselves; babies in real life do not. The details are divided below into three general categories and several more subcategories. Space is left for you to fill in additional information by checking with parents, doctors, agencies, stores, and friends with children to get a clearer picture of the details.

Concerns:		
Medical	*Financial*	*Relationship*
choosing a doctor	insurance	parenting skills
	hospital costs	
prenatal care— nutrition, rest, and exercise	doctor costs	
	child care if I work	reflecting self-esteem to the child
	maternity clothes	
immunizations	formula	
	bottles	
	diapers	
	baby clothing	
	crib	
	blankets	discipline and limits
	sheets	
	car seat	

So, where will *you* fit a baby in your life? Taking time now to think this through will help you when you face choices that affect the future. **Write about your feelings and thoughts, your timing and circumstances.** You will imprint a little soul and generations beyond by your example and ability to cope with all that bearing and raising a child (or grandchild) entails.

Additional Resources:

Teaching Children Joy and *Teaching Children Responsibility,* both by Linda and Richard Eyre
So You Want To Succeed As A Parent, by Charles B. Beckert
Is Anyone Out There Building Mother's Self-Esteem? by Marilynne Todd Linford
The Way Mothers Are, a children's book by Mariam Schlein

I LEARNED TO TALK
WHEN I WAS TWO

(What more is there to communication?)

Profiles

Carrie is afraid to express her true feelings. When asked specifically, she replies, "I don't know" or "Nothing."

Amanda lacks the skills for effective self-expression. She feels like everything she says comes out wrong.

Jolene pushes others around verbally in order to have her way; she doesn't have many friends.

Communication means more than speaking to someone else. It means being honest with ourselves.

* * *

The more honest our communication with ourselves and others, the more possible it is to feel loved and valued, to be healthy, and to learn how to more effectively solve our problems.

* * *

To communicate honestly we must be willing to practice and take risks. That can be scary. We enhance our self-esteem by our willingness to be open to new possibilities—trying new skills of communication, for example—and then practicing them until they become our own.

Jo Ann Larsen, a newspaper columnist, states: "We have all watched people who speak to each other with loving and supportive tones, who work out their differences without fussing and fuming. These people habitually use certain responses that nurture the positives and allow them to talk and share and work out their problems. A number of these responses are actually skills we can learn and use to create good feelings in any relationship."

These skills or keys to emotional honesty can help us express what we want to have happen. In this chapter we include information related to sending "I" messages, communicating nonverbally, listening, avoiding mindreading, and making simple requests. Effective communication skills will not only help you in your family relationships but in your work relationships as well. Remember, new skills take practice, practice, practice! So look for opportunities to use these concepts every day.

Sending "I" messages

If we want to be effective in our communication with others, we need to practice being emotionally honest. In the first chapter we introduced the concept of expressing

> " I want . . ."
>
> " I feel . . ."
>
> "What I want to have happen is . . ."

These "I" messages help us identify what is happening to us. They are a contrast to "you" messages, which almost always blame, criticize, or evaluate. In our associations with others, it's more common to give "you" messages:

> "You make me mad."
>
> "You are to blame for what happened."
>
> "You did that all wrong!"

"I" messages help us understand ourselves. When we express what we feel instead of blaming someone else for what we're feeling, we are taking responsibility for our communication. That is the beginning of emotional honesty. It's important, also, to take responsibility for *how* we talk about our feelings and avoid abrasive, sarcastic, and hostile tones of voice.

Watch your communication for the next few days to see if you use mostly

"you" messages
or
"I" messages.

In the following examples, try changing each **"you"** message to an **"I"** message.	
Example: **"You make me mad when you leave the papers on the floor."**	**"I feel upset when the papers are left on the floor."**
1. "You don't ever to talk to me."	1.
2. "You never help clean the room."	2.
3. "You're so inconsiderate."	3.
4. "You don't ever wash your own dishes."	4.
5. "You don't like me."	5.
6. "You give me a headache."	6.
7. "You _____	7.
8. "You _____	8.
9. "You _____	9.
10. "You _____	10.

Anytime you give an "I" message that describes heavy feelings such as "I felt abandoned at the party and wondered whether you really wanted to be with me," shift immediately to a listening stance. Be ready to listen to—and understand—the problem your message has caused the other person.

Communicating nonverbally

We usually view communication as a verbal skill, not realizing that there is much more to giving and receiving a message. *How* we express the message is much more important than *what* we say. The speaking part of communication is only a small part—less than ten percent of the message. Most of our communication takes place nonverbally with our tone of voice and body language (eye contact, posture, facial expressions, and gestures).

Here is a list of nonverbal cues. After each one, identify the feeling you think is being portrayed.

Flashing eyes   Feeling _____
Questioning eyes   Feeling _____
Laughing eyes   Feeling _____

Smiling   Feeling _____
Biting lips   Feeling _____
Grinding teeth   Feeling _____

Quick movements   Feeling _____
Slow movements   Feeling _____

Toe tapping   Feeling _____
Foot stomping   Feeling _____

Slouching   Feeling _____
Standing tall   Feeling _____

Relaxed stance   Feeling _____
Invading stance   Feeling _____

Pointing   Feeling _____
Jabbing   Feeling _____

When we are not being honest about how we are feeling, our nonverbal cues give us away. We may say one thing but communicate something else nonverbally. Others won't know what message to believe—our verbal message or the nonverbal one. Usually the true message is the nonverbal one. It takes practice to recognize when we are giving mixed messages and learn to match verbal messages with our nonverbal messages.

Can you think of more nonverbal cues?
Write others you recognize in yourself and in the people you know.

Listening—the receiving skill

What happened
when I became aware
of nonverbal cues?

No matter what our experiences with listening have been, listening is a skill that can be learned. It involves commitment to the person with whom we are communicating, and it requires our full attention. Listening is not just a physical response to hearing sound; it also involves giving feedback to the other person, so that it is clear that we understood what was said. Below is a list of reasons to become a good listener. List any others you can think of also.

- It will win you new friends and make your existing friends like you more.

- It creates a perspective for both parties' concerns.

- It promotes objectivity—the ability to step back and look at yourself and/or the situation without judgment or fear.

- It enhances empathy—seeking to understand where the other person is coming from.

- It brings positive feelings into a relationship—the effort you make to listen is positive feedback and automatically (although not immediately) causes the other person to want to reciprocate.

Remember that learning to listen takes practice!

1. In conversation, observe both your partner's and your nonverbal cues, while in the act of listening.
What happened:

2. In conversation, practice rephrasing ("What I hear you saying is . . ." or "You mean . . .", etc.), after each comment the other person makes, then make your own comment.
What happened:

3. In a situation with a friend, commit yourself to understanding (not necessarily agreeing with) your friend's feelings or point of view. Listen, but do not own, the problem. Avoid advising, attacking, judging, blaming, lecturing, or defending yourself.
What happened:

Avoiding mindreading

According to Richard Eyre, most problems we face and most of the unhappiness we experience result from our natural tendency to **"look into mirrors."** In other words, we tend to see all situations, all people, and all circumstances in terms of how these things will affect *us*. We look at another person and see the mirror of our own concerns: "What can he do for me?" or "Will she like me?" We look at a situation or an event, but often what we see is the mirror of what we can gain or lose by it: "What can I get out of this?" or "How will this make me look?" (*Teaching Children Sensitivity*, p. 20).

Mirrors have no depth. We see only the surface of ourselves when we look in them. When we see all situations, people, and circumstances only in terms of ourselves, we are usually making assumptions about what other people are thinking or doing. Another name for this is "jumping to conclusions," and it can cause trouble in a variety of ways. We might assume, for example, that we know what someone else is thinking: "He's mad at me, I'm sure" or "There's no point in asking; I know what she'll say." **Later, we may discover we were wrong.** Mind reading works the other way, too, when we assume that others should be able to read our minds: "He should have known I was upset" or "They should have realized I wanted that assignment." **Even though we sometimes make good guesses, human beings cannot read minds.**

Look at the two lists of words below. Circle one word from the second list to match the situation from the first list.

I Observe a Person	I Think the Person Is
Running down the street	Fearful . . . or exercising
Shouting at someone	Angry . . . or getting someone's attention
Eating a sundae	Hungry . . . or anxious
Drawing a picture	Working . . . or doodling
Talking with a child	Scolding . . . or praising
Being up at night	Watching TV . . . or unable to sleep
Jumping into a car	Late for appointment . . . or looking for someone
Talking to an attorney	Getting information . . . or filing a lawsuit

You may wonder how you would make the right match. In reality, you needed more information to make the decision. We make assumptions about what other people do and expect them to read our minds. Often we spend a lot of time futilely trying to make connections out of context because we don't have or give enough information. In the process of communication, we must recognize that mind reading is not effective!

Requesting, negotiating

Some relationships make it easy to give and receive. In fact, we like to think that those who are close to us will know us well enough to know when we want something. We become hesitant or apologetic about making requests of others. This is because we are:

nagging ("How many times do I have to ask . . . ?")

pleading ("Just this once, would you help little ol' me?")

manipulating ("If you loved me, you'd . . .")

It is easy for us to make requests without stating our wants directly. But to go one step further and explain,

"I want . . ."

is critical because it gives information to the listener. Without giving this information, it's easy to put the listener on the defensive. The statement, "I want . . ." eliminates confusion about control or duty or obligation often associated with requests. We can know we are making requests instead of demands when we respect the listener's freedom to choose what he or she will do in response.

Sometimes we think we are negotiating with another person when we really want the solution to be one way—our way. In the negotiation process both parties will come away winners. The compromise or decision will satisfy both people; otherwise it is not negotiation. The skills we want to be aware of while negotiating are giving "I" messages and listening to others without interruption while they are talking.

Respond to:

HOW I FEEL about making requests:

HOW I FEEL when someone makes a demand of me:

HOW I WOULD LIKE the negotiation process to be with a partner or close friend:

What I want to improve on in my communication with other people:

Additional Reading:

Your Perfect Right
by
Robert Alberti
and
Michael Emmons

Teaching Children Sensitivity
by
Linda and Richard Eyre

You Just Don't Understand
by
Deborah Tannen

WHAT I DID
FOR PLAY
MAY BE
WHAT I WORK
BEST AT

Pretending

Close your eyes and pretend you are nine years old again. It's summer vacation time, and you've just returned from a swimming lesson. The rest of the day is yours. What will you do?

Quick! Jot down whatever ideas come to mind:

What did you decide to do? Climb a tree? Read a book? Take a close look at the activities you selected. Now take a few moments to recall as many other things as possible that you enjoyed doing—for recreation or at school—during your childhood. Write down as many as you can remember.

Look carefully at what you have written and ask yourself: What themes emerge?

Seldom when we've grown up do we look back to our childhood and what we did for play as an assessment of job skills. Yet those childhood activities can provide clues about what we love—and what we love doing deserves to be part of our adulthood also. In the following chapter, we will look at work as something to enjoy; explore people, things, and information preferences; interview someone in a field of interest; and imagine our perfect day. Too many of us are doing what we think we "should" do for work and not what we want. When we figure out what we love to do and want to do for work and incorporate it into our lives, we attain a greater measure of energy and satisfaction.

Growing up

Growing up for most of us means that we will work for a living at some time in our lives. It might happen when we are teenagers or when we are older. It just depends on when we have to start taking care of ourselves financially.

You probably hear complaints from working people and may think that a job is something to be endured until the weekend when you can have time to pursue your hobbies and do what you *really* enjoy— right? Unfortunately, most working people do take that approach to employment. We learn these attitudes from television sitcoms and from family and friends.

You may have noticed, however, that there are people who seem to genuinely enjoy their occupations and work very hard at them. The reason is that these people—the ones who are truly successful in more than finances—have made one or more of their favorite activities their paying work. This is not to suggest that they don't work hard; they may work harder—and more effectively—than anyone else. But they do so precisely because they are doing work that calls upon their best talents, refines their natural skills, and provides results that they find most rewarding.

Now, here's a piece of good news: **With some thought, careful planning, and adequate preparation, the fun and enjoyment you had when you played as a child can be yours again in the world of paid work!** Take a minute now to think of someone you know who really loves his or her work, and does it very well.

The person's name is

His/her occupation is

I can tell that this person loves his/her work, because s/he

Some of the rewards this person receives from his/her work are

---

Make a goal right now to prepare yourself well enough that someday someone could fill in those blanks using your name, your occupation, and the rewards you enjoy.

People, things, or information/ideas

For the moment, let's review your favorite childhood activities and decide what skills and qualities you possessed back then that will indicate your occupational strengths. According to Richard Bolles, author of *What Color Is Your Parachute?* you can categorize your skills and abilities by whether they deal with **people, things, or information/ideas** (pp. 224–228). Some will involve two or all three. Here's an example:

> Susan, at age fourteen, loved to read *Teen* magazine. She had a wonderful English teacher and thoroughly enjoyed her writing class at school. Sometimes, Susan would spend her free time creating a magazine she entitled *Preteener*, for her little sister, age eleven. Following the approach and style of *Teen* magazine and adding some of her own twists and turns, Susan had great fun turning out a new issue of her magazine. It didn't seem to matter that her only reader, a non-paying "subscriber" at that, was little sister Carol. The fun was in the writing!

If Susan were completing the following exercise, she would write something like the example listed below. Following her example, complete the exercise for yourself and determine whether the things you did as a child were oriented toward people, information, or things.

Things I did for fun	People	Things	Information/Ideas
Created my own "magazine"	*about and for*		*Fiction, articles, editorials*

Now look closely at your analysis of favorite activities from childhood. Pretend that you're your mother, father, spouse, sister, teacher, close friend—or any outside observer, for that matter—evaluating your responses. Ask yourself: What jobs or professions do I think this person would do well at, based on what she did for fun? **List a few possibilities below:**

I think this person would be a good

I'd love to become a . . .

Let's go back to Susan's example. Clearly, she liked to write. According to her teachers, she was pretty good at it, too. That skill alone opens a host of possible career options—editor, scriptwriter, journalist, to name just three. Her interest in magazine production certainly is a possibility—but to stop there would be to miss an opportunity to delve deeper into her options. What other jobs might she be suited for?

As it happens, Susan chose to concentrate her energies in the field of training and development. She now spends her time creating instructional materials. Occasionally, she actually trains individuals and classes, using the products she has developed. What brought her such pleasure and fulfillment as a child and teenager—writing, creating, sharing, developing, and physically handling the objects of her craft—now brings her the same satisfactions, plus an income. She does get weary from time to time after a day's work, but it's the kind of weary a person gets from a day of "delightfully hard" work. Rarely does she experience the fatigue of boredom on the job.

Now it's time to go back to the short list of possibilities you noted on the previous page. Do you agree that the jobs listed there indicate your true interests and skills? By now, you've probably thought of several other options you could add. Take a few moments now to identify other careers you could pursue, noting why. What details about you and your background supports each choice?

Be as creative as you can, asking yourself again and again, "What would I really love to do for play—and money?" What do I know about myself already that suggests I can succeed there?

I'd love to become a _____

because _____

_____

I'd love to become a _____

because _____

_____

I'd love to become a _____

because _____

_____

Interviewing for information

As you begin to read and seriously think about the career choices you have, you'll uncover a variety of suggestions that will help you really find out what options best suit you. One of the finest ideas of all is the "information interview." This involves:

- Identifying a field that interests you.
- Beginning to collect a list of names of people who are already working in that field or occupation.
- Contacting a few of those people and asking for 15 minutes of their time, during which you can ask questions about what it's really like to be a professional in that area.

SAMPLE QUESTIONS

1. How long have you worked in this profession?
2. How did you prepare for your occupation?
3. Did you perform an apprenticeship or internship?
4. What would you recommend I do to learn more about entering this field?
5. Will you describe a typical work day for me?

After you've met and talked with a few such people, you will probably form one or two opinions: You'll think either—

(1) Wow! This is a terrific job and I can't wait to start preparing for a similar one myself, or
(2) This isn't exactly what I thought this field was like. I guess I'd better explore other possibilities.

You'll never find out until you **Seek** (really look, and look hard!), **Knock** (go where you need to get information), and **Ask** (question the people who can tell you what you want to know).

You may not be aware of the wide variety of choices open to you. Visit your school counselor or librarian, and request help finding a source that lists occupations, noting desirable aptitudes and necessary skills or qualifications. Read books on the subject. There are literally thousands out there in libraries and bookstores and counselors' offices just waiting for you to discover them.

Date	Books I've Read	People I've Talked To	Outcomes and Feelings

Imagining the perfect workday

Congratulations! You're on your way. Now it's time for you to put yourself into the picture of success. One way to do that is to vividly imagine a day in your future when you are working successfully at your chosen occupation. By writing your journal (or your personal history) in advance, you will find a wonderful sense of direction and enthusiasm.

Here's what we mean: Schedule some time when you can be alone, uninterrupted, and well rested. Plan on at least an hour or so. Sit back, close your eyes, and relax. Imagine, in as much detail as you can, the most typical and fantastic workday you can. Don't hold anything back; pretend that you've completed all the necessary education or training, and that you're enjoying the rewards of accomplishment and success.

Starting with what you choose to wear and eat for breakfast and ending with the last page of the novel you may read just before you fall asleep, describe the people, schedule, events —and feelings—of your day:

_____
_____
_____
_____
_____
_____
_____
_____
_____
_____
_____
_____
_____
_____
_____
_____
_____
_____
_____

(You may need to add some blank paper and write pages and pages.)

There. You've imagined it. Now, go make it come true!

Additional Reading

The Truth About You: Discover What You Should Be Doing With Your Life
by Arthur Miller and Ralph Mattson

The Alphabetized Occupations Finder
by John Holland

If You Don't Know Where You're Going, You'll Probably End up Somewhere Else
by David Campbell

Do What You Love, the Money Will Follow
by Marsha Sinetar

Work in the New Economy: Careers and Job Seeking into the 21st Century
by Robert Wegmann, Robert Chapman, and Miriam Johnson

HAVE I LOST MY TURN ONCE I'M CALLED MOM?

Profiles

Julie's husband died suddenly leaving her alone with five small children and too little life insurance.

Beth felt she needed to work to help out when Paul was laid off, but she couldn't find a job.

Sylvia and Jordan divorced after twenty years of marriage. Sylvia had been home managing family and children and felt she had no marketable skills.

When we dream of the future, we see loving family relationships, our children growing up, everything going just fine, and the future taken care of. We may not anticipate working full-time after having a family; yet on the average, women (regardless of their circumstances) will work at least twenty-six years of their lives, often in low-paying, clerical, or service jobs. Women who do not marry will work approximately forty-five years of their lives. It pays—literally—to decide how you will finish school or upgrade your skills.

When the opportunity to marry and raise a family comes along, most women fit it into their plans. When babies come, so do night feedings and diapers, more laundry and cleaning; a woman's focus may almost exclusively change to husband and children. As each child arrives, more time is needed to manage family concerns, and plans to finish school (and the self-confidence to do so) may fade.

Even if that happened to you, your decision to have children when you did was probably the best time for you and must not be discounted. And if children haven't been part of your life, you may still yearn for them. The circumstances of our lives are individual and the decisions are just as individual. You have the ability to work out your own timing and what is best for you, so give yourself credit for what you've done with your life so far.

Thinking ahead, though, is still practical; maintaining job skills or receiving training in a timely manner is more possible than we usually anticipate. In this chapter, we encourage you to consider your own personal growth, look for opportunities to update or maintain skills you have developed throughout your life, look at skills you can transfer from home into the workplace, validate what you do best, and write out a life plan as a way to look ahead.

Allowing personal growth

After taking care of family needs for a number of years, many women find they need to return to school, upgrade now obsolete skills, or work part-time to make ends meet. Because business and technology are changing so rapidly, additional training is critical. Some women's circumstances allow for full-time schooling; for some a need to become the breadwinner immediately means moving into a full-time program in order to finish soon. Others start back to school one class at a time. Still others find they need to re-examine their earlier career goals because they now have different interests.

The important thing to realize is that there is a way to achieve personal growth goals when you decide what you want to do. It's important to plan for personal growth throughout the various stages of your life. If we are serving others from an "empty bucket" because we haven't taken time for ourselves, we'll feel fatigued without knowing why.

It may be difficult to think about how you will reach your goals. If you develop a plan, however—to stay licensed, keep up with new information in your chosen field, or even to complete one class at a time—you may find that making progress in your personal life spills over and helps you feel more fulfilled as a wife and mother also.

Write a list below of the most important things you want to do.

For your family	For yourself

Updating and maintaining marketable skills

Within our neighborhoods and communities, there are dozens of ways for mothers to interact with others. You may serve as PTA president, church youth teacher, chair of the March of Dimes, political candidate campaigner, or co-op neighborhood preschool teacher. You may organize your husband's computer or bookkeeping system on the side.

The important thing to remember is that there are opportunities in every field that interests you to do volunteer work, talk to people about what they are doing, and turn an interest into a worthwhile career. Service opportunities and leadership opportunities abound. We are not required to do or be all things, but we can be involved in a way that will keep us in touch with our field(s) of interest.

EXERCISE   Fill in the spaces in this brainstorming activity with your own ideas.

Field	Community	Education	Church	Home	Business	People
Journalism, Literature	write for the local newspaper, Be a library volunteer	teach a class	write plays	write family histories, keep a journal	write or read newsletters	write letters
Sports, Physical Therapy	play on a community team					
Computer Science, Mathematics	attend or teach workshops					
Crafts, Arts, Graphics	teach a class					
Dance, Theater	choreograph a musical					
Engineering, Law, Business	serve on public or political committee					
Medicine, Psychology, Social work	volunteer at crisis center or rest home					

Use your own creativity, ask professionals in a certain field, contact community volunteers, friends, or church leaders. You will be surprised to find that almost everyone will have at least one idea. Your ability to generate ideas will increase as you push yourself to gather ideas for maintaining marketability and developing skills.

Transferring skills

When a homemaker must move into the work force after years of working in the home, she may feel uncertain about how she will make the transition. During years of child raising and home management, though, she will have developed many desirable skills. "People skills," for example, are critical in any circumstance; homemaking years involve keeping track of and working with people in a variety of ways.

Organizing a home is similar to organizing a business. Mothers learn to keep track of several things at once—talking on the telephone while fixing dinner, listening to one child practice while working with another child on homework. Or they may be checking the wash, monitoring housework and watering the garden while helping a group of teenagers with a service project of baking six dozen cookies in an hour.

The following is a list of homemaking activities and their companion work skill areas. List any others you can think of. Star (*) your best attributes. (These skills can be useful on a resume.)

Homemaking	Working outside the home
Do household chores under your own initiative	Work with minimal supervision
Deal with tantrums and emergencies	Work under pressure
Maintain schedule for family members	Plan/delegate
Balance checkbook	Utilize money management or math skills
Do things thoroughly	Check completeness/accuracy
Finish what you start	Complete projects
Improve the ways things are done	Develop new or improved procedures
Initiate new projects	Initiate ideas
Compile lists, do weekly cleaning and laundry	Perform repetitive tasks
Quote facts from memory	Remember information
_____	_____
_____	_____
_____	_____
_____	_____
_____	_____

What you do best

Experience—whether in the home managing a family, providing a community service, or in an employment situation—will give you additional skill-developing opportunities. These help you know where your interests lie. For instance, you may like to organize information in a creative manner. Or you may like to fix things for other people. Below are six general areas into which you can categorize various responsibilities. Throughout your life you may develop expertise in each area.

Circle the phrases that identify things you like to do. Then identify your top three areas.

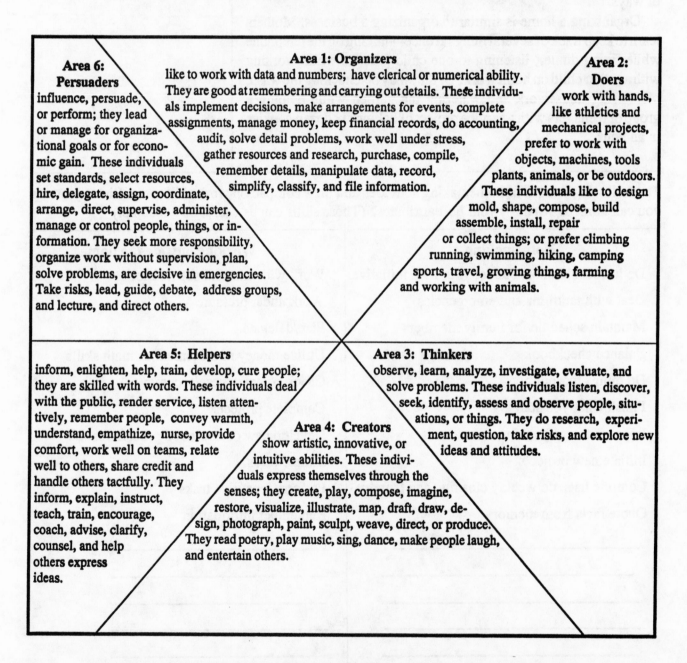

Area 6: Persuaders influence, persuade, or perform; they lead or manage for organizational goals or for economic gain. These individuals set standards, select resources, hire, delegate, assign, coordinate, arrange, direct, supervise, administer, manage or control people, things, or information. They seek more responsibility, organize work without supervision, plan, solve problems, are decisive in emergencies. Take risks, lead, guide, debate, address groups, and lecture, and direct others.

Area 1: Organizers like to work with data and numbers; have clerical or numerical ability. They are good at remembering and carrying out details. These individuals implement decisions, make arrangements for events, complete assignments, manage money, keep financial records, do accounting, audit, solve detail problems, work well under stress, gather resources and research, purchase, compile, remember details, manipulate data, record, simplify, classify, and file information.

Area 2: Doers work with hands, like athletics and mechanical projects, prefer to work with objects, machines, tools plants, animals, or be outdoors. These individuals like to design mold, shape, compose, build assemble, install, repair or collect things; or prefer climbing running, swimming, hiking, camping sports, travel, growing things, farming and working with animals.

Area 5: Helpers inform, enlighten, help, train, develop, cure people; they are skilled with words. These individuals deal with the public, render service, listen attentively, remember people, convey warmth, understand, empathize, nurse, provide comfort, work well on teams, relate well to others, share credit and handle others tactfully. They inform, explain, instruct, teach, train, encourage, coach, advise, clarify, counsel, and help others express ideas.

Area 4: Creators show artistic, innovative, or intuitive abilities. These individuals express themselves through the senses; they create, play, compose, imagine, restore, visualize, illustrate, map, draft, draw, design, photograph, paint, sculpt, weave, direct, or produce. They read poetry, play music, sing, dance, make people laugh, and entertain others.

Area 3: Thinkers observe, learn, analyze, investigate, evaluate, and solve problems. These individuals listen, discover, seek, identify, assess and observe people, situations, or things. They do research, experiment, question, take risks, and explore new ideas and attitudes.

It may take you some time to figure out what you do best, and that's just fine.

Timing and life planning

Although we like to compare ourselves with other people at the same ages and stages to see if we're "doing things right," timing is an individual concept. It's just like growing up. You may have had your growth spurt early and towered over all your friends—even the boys. Or you wondered if you would ever grow tall enough to not be mistaken for a ten-year-old. After awhile, you learned that growth is a personal and unique function. Timing, in terms of personal goals and plans, is just like that—it's different for each person.

On the following page is an outline for planning your life in three different areas of five-year blocks. If you have children and a husband, plot their ages along with your own. Here is an example:

Year	Self	Thomas	Kristen	Jennie	Spencer	Relationship Goals	Financial Goals	Personal Goals
1990	39	14	13	11	9			
1991	40	15	14	12	10	Help teens	Braces paid	Masters
1992	41	16	15	13	11	develop	for	degree
1993	42	17	16	14	12	independence		
1994	43	18	17	15	13			
1995	44	19	18	16	14	Plan	Savings	
1996	45	20	19	17	15	raquetball	for	
1997	46	21	20	18	16	and other	college,	
1998	47	22	21	19	17	activites	weddings,	Take voice
1999	48	23	22	20	18	w/husband	etc.	lessons
2000	49		23	21	19			
2001	50			22	20			
2002	51			23	21			Sing in
2003	52				22			community
2004	53				23			choir
2005	54							
2006	55							
2007	56							
2008	57							
2009	58							
2010	59						home paid	
2011	60						off	

Timing—figuring it out—takes time and patience. We are busy accomplishing things—working and playing. We seem to have to hurry, do more, and do more faster. We live in a world where it's easy to think we can have everything happen right on schedule, just the way we want. Life happens differently, though. It's not always fast, not always the way we want or when we want.

Someone once said that **"Life is what happens to you while you were making other plans."** Life gives us many opportunities to learn and grow. Everything we learn and endure can be for our good and can give us experience. From our experience, we gain knowledge. Knowledge, properly applied, becomes wisdom.

Year	Self	Husband	Child	Child	Child	Child	Relationship Goals	Financial Goals	Personal Goals

Seasons

Too often we look at our lives with only a five- or ten-year perspective. We see what we are *not* doing now and start to panic, thinking that there just isn't enough time to do it all. If we take a look at the possibility of filling our whole life with meaningful activities and relationships, though, we may find more satisfaction in what we can do *now*.

Think of life as a whole, a circle.

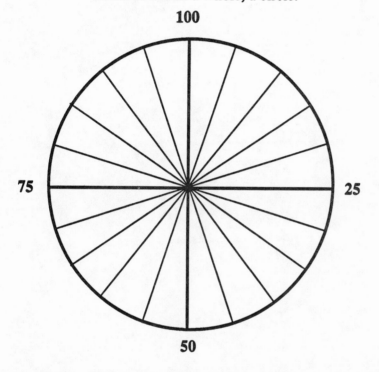

100

75

25

50

Consider what goals can best be accomplished at certain ages. Having children in your twenties and thirties, for example, is most often healthier for you and your baby than giving birth in your earlier or later years. Education and exercise fit well into all ages, and have been found to be excellent activities to keep the mind and body from degenerating. Look at the years in the previous chart, and determine what years will allow you the most physical mobility (children grown, in school, or no longer living at home), more financial discretion (home paid for, higher earnings, retirement). Advances to increase the quality of life and expected lifespan continue to be made. It is up to you whether or not you will enjoy your whole life from beginning to end.

Additional Reading

Passages
by Gail Sheehy

Lifeprints
by Grace Baruch,
Rosalind Barnett,
& Caryl Rivers

Gift from the Sea
by
Anne Morrow Lindbergh

How to Get Control of Your Time and your Life
by Alan Lakein

FINANCIAL REALITIES

(The hidden cost of independence)

Profiles

Anita was frustrated. Every time she needed a little extra money for fun, her parents would suggest she get a job. She didn't want to get a job. She had thought that paying for her expenses was their responsibility.

Evelyn and Richard bought new living room furniture, a television, and stereo when they got married. When the baby was born several months later, they found that some unanticipated medical problems weren't covered in their medical insurance. Soon they were getting behind in the furniture payment. Medical bills were mounting up. Creditors were calling. Richard decided to drop out of school and look for full-time work but could only find a minimum-wage job.

Lorraine's husband had always assured his wife that there would be plenty of money when they retired (or, if anything were to happen to him, from his life insurance policy). They were also entitled to social security. When he died, though, she found that his retirement was a small percentage of his monthly salary. And several years earlier, her husband had borrowed against his life insurance to remodel their home and had not repaid the loan. Even *with* social security, Lorraine found herself living on about $450 per month.

While growing up, we don't usually worry much about how the refrigerator is filled every week or where the money comes from for house payments, new clothes, and medical bills. We may not see the pressures our parents feel and simply assume that when *we're* parents we'll have a perfect job that provides plenty of money for our needs. When we marry and grow older, many of us still assume that the men in our lives will make sure we are taken care of.

Those are some pretty big assumptions. Prince Charming just may not arrive on cue, or he may turn out to be less than financially secure. Some women face making financial decisions for the first time when they become widows. How will you cope with financial decisions you thought you would never have to face?

Following are some ideas to increase your awareness and help you plan how you will handle your financial future—whatever age you are right now. They include looking at the cost of living, assessing your earning power, considering well-paying job options, and being financially responsible for credit and debt.

Looking at the cost of living

ITEMS	AT THE PRESENT		AT RETIREMENT AGE	
	with family	alone	with family	alone
GROCERIES Food Nonfood items Cleaning supplies Miscellaneous				
HOUSING Rent/mortgage Utilities Phone Furniture Maintenance Laundry				
INSURANCE Life insurance Car insurance Medical insurance				
TRANSPORTATION Car Gas Maintenance				
PAYMENTS Credit cards				
CLOTHING				
OTHER EXPENSES Entertainment Personal items Savings Charitable contributions Education Other				
Total monthly costs				

Your earning power

You may have had a part-time job while you were in high school and a full-time job in the summer. You may have worked at a fast-food place, a retail or convenience store, in a warehouse, or on an assembly line. You may now be employed as a secretary or as a licensed nurse practitioner. There are a number of entry-level jobs available. Without training, though, it may be difficult for you to earn more per hour than an entry-level wage. On a yearly basis, working at $4.00 per hour, you would make about $8,000 annually. Could you live on $8,000? Could you raise a family on that income?

Below is a list of wages per hour, followed by corresponding monthly and yearly totals. Remember that federal and state taxes and social security are deducted from each check. The monthly and yearly totals are gross (the amount you earned before taxes and social security), not net (take-home) pay.

Wage per hour	Per month	Per year
$4.00	$ 693.33	$ 8,320
4.50	780.00	9,360
5.00	866.67	10,400
5.50	953.33	11,440
6.00	1,040.00	12,480
6.50	1,126.67	13,520
7.00	1,213.33	14,560
7.50	1,300.00	15,600
8.00	1,386.67	16,640
8.50	1,473.33	17,680
9.00	1,560.0	18,720
9.50	1,646.67	19,760
10.00	1,733.33	20,800
10.50	1,820.00	21,840
11.00	1,906.67	22,880
11.50	1,993.33	23,920
12.00	2,080.00	24,960

If you were your own or your family's sole support, how much could you earn per hour if you had to find a job today? Or if you are working now, how much would you need to earn in order to support a family with two children? with four? with six?

Risk versus security

Women take big risks with relationships and small risks financially. They trust that when they marry, someone will take care of them. When it comes to occupations, though, women prefer to stay in traditional areas—the low-paying ones—rather than move into nontraditional areas that may pay more. Nontraditional jobs are those where 25 percent or fewer of the workers in a particular area are women. For instance, more than 90 percent of engineers are men. On the other end of the spectrum, 99 percent of secretaries are women. That doesn't mean you have to be an auto mechanic or a construction worker, although some women enjoy those jobs. It does mean that when you look at your interests, consider other options besides secretary, nurse, and teacher.

The low-wage, sex-segregated jobs in which the majority of women work is called the "pink-collar ghetto." Did you know that **the 1987 poverty-level income for a family of four was $223 per week,** and that all of the following traditional women's occupations provided even less than $223 per week in 1987?

- retail sales clerk..... $192/week
- waitress.................. $178/week
- cashier.................... $183/week
- food worker........... $149/week
- nursing aide........... $212/week
- teacher's aide......... $200/week.

Part-time and temporary jobs typically provide few or no benefits, limited job security, few opportunities for advancement, and average only 50 percent of the hourly earnings of full-time workers.

Whatever your interests, begin to look for alternatives that will pay you enough to support yourself and a family.

The "feminization of poverty" is both real and tragic. This term is used to define the majority of the poor in our country who are women with children at home. That is why you want to work hard to prepare for your future by gaining some marketable skills.

Seeking nontraditional options

Do you sew or like detail work? Sewing is similar in many ways to drafting or electronics. Those areas are nontraditional. Do you enjoy balancing your checkbook? Accounting is nontraditional. Are you thinking of being a secretary? Look beyond to becoming a loan or credit officer. In retail careers, nontraditional is being a buyer. Be the boss. These possibilities are nontraditional. they usually offer more money and greater flexibility

The *Occupational Outlook Handbook* lists many job options currently available. Nontraditional careers include architect, draftsman, auto mechanic, city bus driver, chemist, computer programmer, computer technician, dietician, engineer, forester, hotel manager, lawyer, mail carrier, physician, physical therapist, pilot, plumber, police officer, school principal, securities sales worker, school counselor, social worker, and welder, to name a few.

Career options I'm considering	Nontraditional options I want to find out about
_____	_____
_____	_____

People I can talk to about other options

- Teachers
- Parents
- Adult friends
- Employer
- Career counselors
  (school or community college)

In her book *How to Succeed in Business Without Being a Man,* Carol Shelton Walker comments, "Like me, many of you women must take care of yourselves, or help your husbands earn a living. Why spend eight hours a day working for little pay if there is a way you can control your own terms and decide what your salaries will be? For me it became simply a matter of knowing that since I had to make money, I might as well make a lot as a little," (p. 14).

Being financially responsible

Taking responsibility, a measuring stick of adulthood, is a regular theme in this workbook. Below is a list of behaviors. Some are responsible, some are not. Determine your attitude by checking the frequency of your behavior: Is this something you always, sometimes, or never do?

	Sometimes	Never	Always
• Pay bills on time			
• Overspend			
• Complete work assignments			
• Pay only if you have money			
• Bounce checks			
• Speak directly to someone about a problem			
• Blame someone else for your problem			
• Do what you say you'll do			
• Complain about a problem			
• Call if you'll be late			
• Make excuses			

Your Credit History

How you handle money will eventually determine your "credit rating," a record kept on file at your local credit bureau noting money you have borrowed and whether or not you have repaid it on time. Unless you have borrowed money, used a credit card, or have been denied credit, you probably do not have a credit rating. Your credit rating will be under your name, or if you are married it may be under both your name and your husband's (if you have joint credit). If you have been late in your payments or have a delinquent doctor bill, this will be part of your credit rating.

It is still the case that many married women do not know what their credit rating is or if they even have one. Both bad and good credit ratings can follow you after a separation or divorce. When a woman becomes a widow and has never used credit, she may have a difficult time borrowing money or getting a credit card in her own name.

Using credit

Because of the ease of qualifying for credit, you may want everything right now—stereo, car, furniture, home, etc. You may be impatient to have it all like your parents, forgetting that the material things they enjoy have been accumulated over a lifetime.

It takes maturity to accept responsibility for what you owe. If, for any reason, you have difficulty paying a bill, it is your responsibility to contact your creditor—in writing and by phone. Creditors are usually willing to work with you in some way, perhaps reducing your payments for a time. If you have been denied credit, you can check your credit report with your local credit bureau by appointment for free. (You can check it anytime for a cost of about $10.00.)

The following exercise will help you assess whether or not you are headed for trouble with credit cards These are danger signs of credit abuse. Take the quiz and see where you stand.

True	False	
___	___	You hide things you buy so your family won't discover them.
___	___	You're a juggler—you put off paying other bills so you can pay your credit card on time.
___	___	You've applied for a second Visa or MasterCard.
___	___	You usually only pay the minimum monthly payment.
___	___	You've used the cash advance on one card to make payments on other credit cards.
___	___	You believe that someday you'll get enough money to pay off all your debts.
___	___	You've received a phone call about your delinquent account.
___	___	You don't know how much you owe within $50.
___	___	The balance in your savings account is shrinking or you are not saving at all.
___	___	You usually borrow from friends or relatives to make ends meet each month.
___	___	Life would be difficult if you lost all your credit cards.

Score: Answer true to six or more, and you're headed for trouble.
Answer true to nine or more and you may have a serious problem.
(*Deseret News*, March 20, 1989, page C1.)

Eliminating debt

Whether you are married or single it is helpful to assess your debt picture every year. To measure your debt—

1. List all of your non-mortgage loans:

car loans   _____

school loans   _____

personal loans   _____

credit card   _____

credit card   _____

credit card   _____

2. Total your average monthly payment for each account.

3. To find your debt rate, divide your monthly take-home pay (net) into your average monthly debt (add two zeros to your debt to make the division easier). The answer will show your percentage of debt— how far in debt you are.

Your monthly take-home pay: $_____

Divided into your average monthly debt: $_____

Your debt rate (percentage):   _____%

10%: Congratulations. You have a firm hand on spending and you're a good credit manager. Continue as you have been doing.

15%: You are in the high-average group. There's no cause for alarm, but you should slow down on your spending and try to get your debt closer to 13%.

20%: You have a problem. You should stop using credit immediately, stop unnecessary spending, and work at reducing your debt.

25%: Red Alert—your home, your car, and your debt are probably eating up 75% of your paycheck. It's time for a dramatic change in lifestyle. You'll probably need professional help.

(*Deseret News*, March 20, 1989, page C1.)

Paying your way through school

"Despite what you may have heard, it's still possible to get enough financial aid to pay for a college education. Some government aid programs have been cut back, but rumors have exaggerated the extent of those cuts—and many colleges have taken up the slack. In fact, the chief stumbling blocks to getting aid may well be unfounded rumors and 'paperwork panic.'

"Paperwork panic strikes when students and their families see the financial forms that have to be filled out to apply for government grants. Of course,it does takes time to complete the forms. And money for college doesn't have to come from a single source; many students put together an aid package from several places. **Here are some of the best sources:**

1. File for a Pell Grant. Based entirely on need, Pell grants range from a high of around $1,800 to a token $100. Although there's no fixed cut-off point in determining eligibility, a four-person family is generally phased out of this program when income exceeds $18,000. To apply for a Pell grant, you must fill in a needs-analysis form, disclosing income and assets. Forms are available from high school guidance counselors and college financial aid offices.

2. Apply for aid through your college or technical school. Colleges administer three federal programs: (1) Supplemental Educational Opportunity Grants ($200 to $2,000 a year) for very low-income students; (2) work-study grants for on- and off-campus employment; and (3) National Direct Student Loans at 5 percent interest for low-income students. Colleges can also supply information about any state tuition aid programs you might be eligible for. In addition, a school may consider making an additional grant from its own scholarship funds. Most such aid is based on need, but nearly 800 colleges give modest merit scholarships.

3. Consider cooperative education. More than 1,000 colleges allow students to combine education with work in a given field. In some cases, semesters of school and semesters of work (at jobs the colleges help arrange) are alternated; in others, students study part-time and work part-time.

4. Take a government-subsidized student loan. The maximum annual loan from participating banks is $2,400 for undergraduates and $5,000 for graduate students (if your family earns less than $30,000). Higher-income students, however, must submit a statement showing financial need. Borrowers pay 9 percent interest on student loans, a 5 percent fee when the loan is made, and often a l percent government insurance fee.

5. Join the armed services or the reserves. The Army, Navy, and Air Force all offer full-tuition scholarships (plus $100-a-month living allowances) to bright students who agree to spend at least four years in the service (as officers) after graduation. These highly competitive scholarships favor science and engineering students, but others may also qualify. Those who enlist directly in the armed services can get tuition assistance for approved part-time study, vocational training, or courses leading to a college degree.

6. Check for special scholarships. Libraries, high school guidance counselors, and college aid officers all have books that explain the requirements for a variety of private scholarships. For example, the Business and Professional Women's Foundation in Washington, D.C., offers scholarships to women twenty-five or older who need help in finishing their education. Most private scholarships are modest, but a few are quite generous. Children and spouses of active, retired, disabled, or deceased service men and women may also qualify for special aid." (Quinn, p. 18)

Seeking financial aid

Some good questions to ask with regard to financial aid include:

1. What are my plans for completing a training program or college degree?

2. What financial needs will I have?

3. How much can I pay for myself (with part-time or full-time work)?

4. What are additional barriers I foresee?

5. What do I want to have happen to me financially? or What are my financial goals?

Part of being financially responsible is committing to be in charge of your financial and credit history—whether you are single or married. Some married women are in financial crisis because they assumed their husband was "taking care of everything," only to learn that they are losing their home, facing bankrupty or a divorce without any idea that anything was wrong. There are some things you can control, and your financial status is one of them.

Additional Reading

How to Succeed in Business Without Being a Man
by Carol Shelton Walker

The Occupational Outlook Handbook
by
the U.S. Department of Labor

Don't Miss Out:
a complete guide to student aid

SPEEDING TICKETS AND OTHER CONSEQUENCES

(Laws of nature, laws of life)

Profiles

Jeri's throat tightened and her fingers gripped the steering wheel as she pulled off to the side of the road. The flashing red and blue lights in her rearview mirror brought an end to thoughts of getting to her appointment on time. She had only been five minutes behind schedule starting out and gambled that by going ten miles over the speed limit she could make up the time. The police officer took his time making out the ticket and gave her a lecture on the hazards of driving at high speeds in residential areas. Now she was forty-five minutes late and angry at herself for having to give up $50 to pay for her impatience.

Brenda confided to her friend Ellen, "It really doesn't matter what I major in, because I just know I'll get married before I graduate. And I won't have to work afterward unless I want to, because I intend to marry rich!" she continued, laughing.

Fifteen years later, Ellen was surprised to find Brenda behind the counter of an all-night convenience store.

"Brenda!" Ellen exclaimed, "I never expected to find you here, of all places!"

Brenda sighed. "Mr. Wonderful hasn't shown up yet, but I keep hoping."

Lynne looked regretfully over her resume. High grades were about all she had to offer as qualifications for a graduate scholarship. As she tried to think back on what experiences she had had in the community, she remembered being elected as president of a major service organization in town. After two weeks, though, she had decided she just couldn't afford to take the time away from her studies, and resigned. Now 10 years later an experience in leadership and service in the community would have been as impressive as a string of A's.

At this point, if you have worked your way through this workbook, you will have an amazing portrait of yourself, your desires, and abilities. This chapter is provided to summarize some of the ideas explored in previous chapters and give you one last bit of encouragement: do what you want within the framework of your own timing—not all at once—and plan for some "taking care of yourself time" throughout the process. So join us in taking a final look at laws and consequences, the skill of life planning, a solution for the fine art of doing too much, looking ahead, and making progress one step at a time.

Laws and consequences

What am I doing in my life that will lead me toward a consequence of good health?

We live with both laws and consequences. When we understand the laws that govern our lives and obey them, we obtain certain rewards. When we try to ignore their reality, we pay a price. Take a law found in nature—gravity, for instance. When we choose to take the stairs or elevator from the third floor to first, we are rewarded by a safe arrival (in most cases). Were we to try to save time by leaping from a third floor window, our descent would be less secure, most likely resulting in death or serious injury.

The consequences of leaping from the third floor are immediate. There are other decisions we make where we won't see the consequences immediately—taking care of our health, for instance. It's easy to be too busy to exercise, and rationalize that there isn't enough room in the refrigerator for fresh fruit and vegetables, or to skip meals to meet deadlines, and then binge all night (because we're so hungry at the end of the day and it helps us unwind while we're watching television). Fifteen years later, we find ourselves asking why we have a weight problem and feel tired all the time.

By not taking time for exercise, proper nutrition, and enough sleep *now*, the consequence is chronic fatigue. In her book *Women and Fatigue*, Dr. Holly Atkinson defines fatigue as "a feeling of having insufficient energy to carry on and a strong desire to stop and rest or sleep—a sign of weariness." She traces the symptom of tiredness to a lack of adequate self-care through exercise, healthy eating habits, and plenty of rest. In addition, women are often unaware of the energy toll they are paying due to the effects of drugs, alcohol, and cigarettes. It will be easy for you when you begin working, going to school, getting married, and having children to get so busy taking care of the details that you eliminate the activities in your life that will give you energy (p. 11).

Similarly, we can choose to learn and obey the laws that govern our personal growth and success—or we can pretend that "everything will work out okay, one way or another." Taking the latter approach is something like jumping into a car without a day of driver's training and heading for a destination—any destination—without a map. "I don't have time for driver's education," the would-be driver complains, searching for the ignition. "Now what are all these pedals and numbers for?"

Life planning—a skill

Take a moment to think of a skill you developed through careful study and repeated practice. Examples might include typing, riding a bicycle, dancing, swimming, or operating a piece of equipment.

What is the skill you're thinking of? Write it here.

_____

What motivated you—made you truly want to develop the skill? Did you want to find a certain job? impress someone? win an award? Think about this carefully and respond.

_____

_____

Describe the feelings you experienced while you were developing the skill—before you had really mastered it.

_____

_____

Describe the feelings you have had since becoming proficient at the skill. _____

_____

By now, it should come as no surprise to you that

life planning is a skill

and, like any other "competency," it must be carefully developed by you, the participant. To leave this most essential activity to chance—like so many people do, unfortunately—is to miss the joy and accomplishment you can know as a result of applied study, effort, and practice.

***

Yes, life successfully lived—like sonatas flawlessly played and landscapes beautifully painted—takes practice.
It's a law.

***

Playing the consequences game

Now it's time to consider the *"what if's."* Complete this exercise thoughtfully. As you answer the questions, resist the temptation to write only the first answer that comes to mind. Write them all, far out as some may seem. Experts say our best answer in a series may well be our last.

1. What are the possible outcomes of *deciding what you want* out of life?

2. What are the possible outcomes of *not deciding what you want* out of life (and just taking it day by day)?

3. What are the possible outcomes of *choosing and carefully maintaining* the major relationships in your life?

4. What are the possible outcomes of simply *"letting relationships happen?"*

5. What are the possible outcomes of *deciding in advance* under what circumstances to have children?

6. What are the possible outcomes of *not worrying* about marriage, pregnancies, and childraising?

7. What are the possible outcomes of *carefully evaluating your strengths and preparing* accordingly for a career?

8. What are the possible outcomes of *making no career plans* and working from one job to another?

You just might be lucky and end up with what you want without much planning or effort. You just might escape without injury from a drive, blindfolded, on the freeway.

Chances are, though, that

You will succeed or fail in direct proportion to your willingness to obey the natural, social, and personal laws upon which success is built.

Doing too much

It's hard work, this *obedience-to-law-plan-your-life-carefully* business. But there's danger, believe it or not, in too much thought and too much work. Reflecting back at life's end, you'll want to remember more than an impressive career portfolio, balanced checkbook, and your "2.3" children who had regular dental checkups. What else do you want to remember?

If she had her life to live over, commentator/humorist Erma Bombeck would have "invited friends over to dinner even if the carpet was stained and the sofa faded . . . burnt the pink candle sculptured like a rose before it melted while being stored . . . cried and laughed less while watching television and more while watching real life" (Bombeck).

Some regrets and resolutions from a few less celebrated but just as real respondents as Ms. Bombeck:

Training director/philanthropist Mary Ellen Edmunds would have "talked on elevators ('lets get together again sometime') . . . sold fish bait longer (I was pretty good at it—and to think I could have doubled profits just by cutting those worms in half!) . . . thrown away junk mail without opening it . . . said 'whee!' more than 'uh-oh.'"

Artist/mother Jerry Christopherson would have "spent more time sketching my children and less time insisting that they clean their bedrooms and tie their shoes."

Instructional scientist/Ph.D. candidate Tracy Watson would have "manned more flights to the moon in a cardboard box with my brother (so what if I was 25 at the time?)."

Avid father/administrator/church leader Richard Heaton plans to "walk more, drive less . . . resist those late night sitcom reruns that leave me brain-dead . . . and get up a little earlier in the morning."

Others would have "not rationed smiles as though they were a limited commodity," . . . "read fewer cereal boxes and more Ralph Waldo Emerson," . . . "not separated joy from work nor work from service," . . . "never diminished a child's enthusiasm and spontaneity by saying 'don't scrunch up your face like that when you laugh,'" . . . "written more letters of thanks than criticism to manufacturers of disposable razors and spaghetti sauce," . . . "dared to 'fall in comitment' without years of premarital analysis," . . . "not said so much about calories or taxes," . . . "worried less about professinal development and more about child development," . . . *extracted every liquid jewel of laughter, love, and learning from this laboratory called Life.*

Living it over/living ahead

You may probably have more of life ahead than you have behind, but it isn't too early to decide now what will be most important to you. Try to imagine life thirty, forty, fifty years from now, and ask yourself—

What accomplishments am I most proud of now that I'm eighty?

How did I make the best use of my natural talents and skills?

Here are some things I'm glad I took time to do/pay attention to/ spend time learning about:

Here are some things that weren't worth worrying about, after all:

117

One step at a time

Some final words of advice. Sometimes when we make plans and look at all there is to do, we get overwhelmed and then it's hard to do anything at all. We get stuck. That's when it's good to break the assignment or task down into manageable pieces and do one step at a time.

Think of something you have to do.

_____

Now break it down into smaller pieces (that take an hour or less to accomplish).

Step 1 _____

Step 2 _____

Step 3 _____

Step 4 _____

and so on. . . .

When you get overwhelmed, remember to ask yourself,

"What is my next step?"

Any plans you make are not set in concrete; you want to be prepared to adapt and make changes where necessary. If you make your plans too firm and too inflexible, they may not turn out exactly as you want; you'll spend lots of energy worrying about what you did wrong. It's important to develop flexibility, remembering that there are often lots of possible outcomes to our plans.

When something goes wrong or seems to have a negative consequence, avoid blaming yourself. Ask yourself,

"How is this a win for me? What am I getting out of this that I couldn't get faster any other way?"

Think of something that didn't work out the way you anticipated.

What did you learn?

What would you do differently?

A final thought

What I have learned about myself through the past twelve chapters?

We have shared our hearts and thoughts with you over the past twelve chapters. Our own experiences have varied, yet we've learned some of the same important lessons about life along the way, namely that (1) we can take initiative in planning our own lives and what we want to have happen without always waiting for permission, (2) taking care of ourselves and loving ourselves is an important part of the service we render to others, and (3) taking time for our own personal growth can bring a wonderful measure of personal satisfaction and contentment into our lives. Our final message to you is:

> *Remember every day to love and accept*
> *yourself where you are right now. Be*
> *gentle with yourself, expect good things*
> *to happen, seek ideas and people who*
> *can assist you along the way, relax a*
> *little, and laugh a lot more. Enjoy the*
> *whole delightful process of life on earth—*
> *all the ups and downs, the accomplishments,*
> *and heartaches—even the tiny moments*
> *when things seem to be just right.*

> *With love,*
> *Karen, Susan, and Jerry.*

Copyright acknowledgments

References

Adkins, C. (1975) "Wacky Wordies," *Games*.

Alberti, R., Emmons, M. (1974) *Your Perfect Right*, San Luis Obispo, CA: Impact.

Beattie, M. (1989) *Beyond Codependency*, New York: Harper & Row.

Bolles, R. (1989) *What Color Is Your Parachute?* Berkeley, Ca: Ten Speed Press.

Borysenko, J. (1987) *Minding the Body, Mending the Mind*, New York: Bantam Books.

Bradshaw, J. (1988) *Bradshaw on the Family*, Deerfield Beach, FL: Health Communication, Inc.

Carkhuff, R., Pierce, R., Cannon, J. (1980) *The Art of Helping*, Amherst: Human Resource Development Press.

Ellsworth, R., Ellsworth, S. (1980) *Getting to Know the Real You*, Salt Lake City: Deseret Book.

Eyre, L., Eyre, R. (1987) *Teaching Children Sensitivity*, New York: Ballantine Books.

Gawain, S. (1979) *Creative Visualization*, New York: Bantam Books.

Helmstetter, S. (1986) *What To Say When You Talk To Yourself*, New York: Pocket Book.

Jeffers, S. (1987) *Feel the Fear and Do It Anyway*, New York: Fawcett Columbine.

Larsen, J. (1991) *I'm a Day Late and a Dollar Short . . . and It's OK*, Salt Lake City: Deseret Book.

L'Engle, M. (1980) *Ring of Endless Light*, New York: Dell Publishing Company.

Olsen, T. (1986) *Aanchor*, Provo: Department of Family Science, Brigham Young University.

Quinn, J. (1983) "Money Facts," *Woman's Day*, (p. 18).

Roger, J. & McWilliams P. (1990) *You Can't Afford the Luxury of a Negative Thought*, Los Angeles, CA: Prelude Press.

Ross, R. (1983) *Prospering Woman*, New York: Bantam Books.

Satir, V. (1976) *Making Contact*, Berkeley, CA: Celestial Arts.

Sher, B. (1979) *Wishcraft*, New York: Ballantine Books.

Smith, V. (Jan 1985) "The Warning Signs of Infidelity," *Ensign*, Salt Lake City: Corporation of the President of the Church of Jesus Christ of Latter-day Saints, (pp. 59–61).

Ueland, Brenda (1987) *If You Want To Write*, St. Paul, MN: Graywolf Press.

Walker, C. (1987) *How to Succeed in Business Without Being a Man*, Salt Lake City: Osmond Publishing.